THE FORMATION OF
THE AMERICAN MEDICAL PROFESSION

The Role of Institutions

1780–1860

THE FORMATION OF
THE AMERICAN MEDICAL PROFESSION

The Role of Institutions, 1780–1860

by

Joseph F. Kett

New Haven and London, Yale University Press, 1968

Copyright © 1968 by Yale University.
Designed by Marvin H. Simmons,
set in Baskerville type,
and printed in the United States of America by
Vail-Ballou Press, Inc., Binghamton, N.Y.
Distributed in Canada by McGill University Press.
All rights reserved. This book may not be
reproduced, in whole or in part, in any form
(except by reviewers for the public press),
without written permission from the publishers.

Library of Congress catalog card number: 68-13914

TO MY MOTHER AND FATHER

PREFACE

The years between 1880 and 1910 witnessed a decisive transformation in American medical practice. First, the establishment of effective state licensing boards barred quacks from the profession. Then American scientists like William H. Welch and William S. Halsted, their horizons broadened by contact with the German laboratory tradition, took the initiative in setting up at Johns Hopkins University the finest hospital and medical school in America. Finally, Abraham Flexner, possibly the most influential Hopkins graduate, declared in 1910 a holy war on the innumerable second- and third-rate American medical schools. By 1920 the foes, mediocrity and incompetence, were ready to come to terms.

The war was won but battles had been lost. Welch, Flexner, and like-minded reformers had to contend with a formidable legacy of low educational standards left by the pre-Civil War generation. Historians have found little to say in defense of medical standards in the 1820 to 1860 period. Medical schools were bad, sometimes incredibly bad. The profession fell in public esteem. Above all, attempts to regulate entrance to the profession collapsed as state after state repealed all penalties on unqualified practitioners in the 1830s and 1840s. Medical practice was opened to all comers. Charlatanism was rampant as the barrier between the educated physician and quack apparently disappeared. The Jacksonian period has been viewed as a Dark Age of the profession—dashing the expectations of an earlier generation, long frustrating attempts at reconstruction by a later generation, and jeopardizing the lives of thousands. "Men dropped down into their places as from clouds," Joseph G. Baldwin wrote in the *Flush Times of Alabama and Mississippi* in 1853.

> Nobody knew who or what they were, except as they claimed, or as a surface view of their characters indicated. Instead of taking to the highway and magnanimously

calling upon the wayfarer to stand and deliver, or to the fashionable larceny of credit without prospect or design of paying, some unscrupulous horse doctor would set up his sign as "Physician and Surgeon" and draw his lancet on you, or fire at random a box of pills into your bowels, with a vague chance of hitting some disease unknown to him, but with a better prospect of killing the patient, whom or whose administrator he charged some ten dollars a trial for his marksmanship.

Baldwin was convinced that his chaotic picture was a reflection of a larger social malaise besetting the Southwest. A new era had set in,

the era of the second great experiment of independence; the experiment, namely, of credit without capital, and enterprise without honesty. The Age of Brass had succeeded the Arcadian period when men got rich by saving a part of their earnings, and lived at their own cost and in ignorance of the new plan of making fortunes on the profits of what they owed . . . "Commerce was king"—a Rag, Tag and Bobtail his cabinet council . . . a period constituting an episode in the commercial history of the world —the reign of humbug, and wholesale insanity, just overthrown in time to save the whole country from ruin.

James Fenimore Cooper noted similar tendencies in the East. In the first stage of taming the frontier, he asserted in *Home as Found* that society was characterized by "fun, toil, neighborly feeling and adventure." The aristocrat readily yielded some of his superiority; the democrat laid claim to an outward show of equality "that he secretly knows, however, is the result of the peculiar circumstances in which he is placed." But this stage is succeeded by another, in which society begins to marshall itself and the ordinary passions have sway. Now the struggles for place that set institutions at defiance commence. Public opinion is too uncultivated to exert a restraining influence. A pell mell ensues as men demand "a consideration that would seem beyond their reach in an older and more regulated society." In this "least inviting condition of society"—

Jacksonian America—deference to superiority is destroyed. Provincialism and aggressive individualism become rampant.

Cooper was in many ways a fogy turned social philosopher. But historians, regardless of their moral evaluation of the thirties and forties, have agreed with him that the age marked a weakening of an older institutional stability, which necessitated a reassertion of more rigid community control after the Civil War. The Jacksonian period, Carl Russell Fish has observed, was "one of the outstanding instances in history of the working of individuals trammeled by a minimum of law and convention." To Frederick Jackson Turner, who saw the age as a triumph of frontier democracy, Andrew Jackson's election conformed to the "drift of tendencies in this New World democracy—a democracy which preferred persons to property, an active share by the people in government to the greater system and efficiency of a scientific administration by experts or by an established elite who dealt with the people from above."

Tocqueville once suggested, however, that while institutions were relatively feeble in America, American society did not run to anarchy. Americans, he noted, had managed to work out, sometimes unconsciously, solutions to the threat of institutional disorganization. I feel that something like this happened in the medical profession and, to show how, I have selected certain topics for close study, specifically licensing, medical organization, medical education, and sectarianism. To the objection that other issues could have been selected I plead *nolo contendere*. But the issues picked are at least significant ones and were so recognized in the nineteenth century. The content of the book, then, falls somewhere between its title and its subtitle. I have not written a chronological study of all aspects connected with the formation of the profession but at the same time I have sought to go beyond an institutional approach. My method has been to use social and intellectual currents as manifested in sectarianism to evaluate the role of institutions.

Paying off one's debts is not usually a pleasant experience but I welcome here the opportunity to acknowledge and thank a number of people who have aided me over the years in preparing this manuscript. Donald Fleming of Harvard University first made me aware of the role of medicine in American society and supervised the thesis version of the book. He kindly consented to read a revised version of the thesis and on all occasions proved himself a keen and demanding critic. Dr. Lloyd G. Stevenson, chairman of the Department of History of Science and Medicine of Yale University, subjected still another revision to a patient and perceptive reading. He has saved me from sundry errors and enormities. A Fulbright scholarship in 1962–63 enabled me to spend time at University College, London, where I benefited from numerous conversations with R. S. Roberts. David Bertelson of the University of California, Berkeley, read the chapter on Thomsonianism and shared with me his rich knowledge of American cultural history in the Jacksonian period. Mrs. Anne Wilde and her colleagues at the Yale University Press made valuable suggestions for improving the book. Any errors that remain are my responsibility.

I am grateful for the courtesy shown me by the following libraries: the library of the New York Academy of Medicine, the New York Historical Society, the South Carolina Historical Society, the Charleston Library Society, the South Carolina State Archives, the library of the Medical College of South Carolina, the South Caroliniana Library of the University of South Carolina, the medical library of the University of Cincinnati, the Cincinnati Historical Society, the library of the Medical and Chirurgical Faculty of Maryland, the Maryland Historical Society, the Maryland Hall of Records at Annapolis, the Enoch Pratt Free Library in Baltimore, the medical library of Tulane University, the Massachusetts Historical Society, the library of the Massachusetts Medical Society, the Boston Medical Library (now part of the Countway Library of Medicine), and the National Medical Library. I would like to single out for special mention Mrs. Lee Jordan of the Cincinnati Historical Society, Mrs. Mandy Fort of the medical library of the University of Cincinnati, Miss Desmond Koster of the medical library of the Medical College of South Carolina, Robert Potter, M.D., who allowed me to use the Minutes of the Medical Society of the County of New York, and William D. Postell of Tulane University who shared with me his exceptional knowledge of southern folk and slave medicine.

I am indebted to Harvard University for providing travel funds and to the faculty research committee of the University of Virginia for both travel and typing funds. My wife, Eleanor H. Kett, provided clerical assistance and other kinds of aid less measurable.

J. F. K.

Charlottesville, Virginia
December 1967

CONTENTS

ONE

The Weak Arm of the Law

*The Doctors have established their Meditial Societyes and have their
State and County Meetings, by which they have so nearly enietlated
[annihilated?] Quacary of all kinds, that a poor man cant git so grate
cures of them now for a ginna, as he could 50 years ago of an old
Squaw for halfe a pint of Rhum. The bisness of a Midwife could be
purformed 50 years ago for halfe a doller and now it costs a poor man
5 hole ones.*

William Manning, The Key of Libberty, *1798*

TUDOR AND STUART PRACTICE

At Christmas time, 1603, John Woolton, medical graduate of Oxford
and established physician of Exeter, England, made the mistake of
his life. He wrote a letter to one Thomas Edwards, a respected
apothecary of the same town, berating him for being, among other
things, unscrupulous, fraudulent, incompetent, and, above all, a
practitioner of medicine. Edwards never wrote back. Instead, he
assembled a mass of testimonials to his skill and honesty and took
his tormentor to court for criminal libel. The case dragged on for
over three years, with a pyramid of depositions and interrogatories
assembled. A decision was finally rendered in Edwards' favor. Poor
Woolton was sentenced to stand in Exeter market place at assize
time with twelve feet of depositions tied around his neck.[1]

Considering that a seventeenth-century Englishman viewed libel
as a Spanish contemporary viewed Socinianism, Woolton might have
counted himself fortunate for such a mild punishment. But medical
graduates elsewhere in England who had any pretensions to keeping

1. R. S. Roberts, "The Personnel and Practice of Medicine in Tudor and Stuart
England. Part I. The Provinces," *Med. Hist.*, 6 (Oct. 1962), 371–74, 363–82; R. S.
Roberts, "The Personnel and Practice of Medicine in Tudor and Stuart England.
Part II. London," *Med. Hist.*, 7 (July 1964), 216–34.

1

a monopoly over internal medicine could not have taken much comfort from the recognized implication of the decision, the vindication of an apothecary's right to practice medicine. Most graduates would have argued that the three orders of physician, surgeon, and apothecary were to be kept separate. A surgeon was to confine himself to the messy jobs, amputations, excisions of cancers, and the like. The apothecary was to be a kind of orderly who carried out the physician's directions, stocking medicinals in his shop and mixing them in his mortar in the combinations called for. The physician was to stand at the head of the profession, diagnosing the disease, prescribing the remedy, but not sullying himself with routine tasks.

Whatever reply to the court a physician might have given, it would not have been especially convincing. For by 1600 the traditional notions of separation did not accurately describe the state of medical practice in England, and had not done so for nearly a century. The vision of figures like Thomas Linacre and other men of the New Learning of an English profession tightly regulated and scientifically advanced on the Italian model had crumbled amidst the economic and social realities of Tudor England.

The failure was not the result of any lack of effort. With the support of Cardinal Wolsey, Linacre had secured passage of a number of laws aimed at realizing a new professional spirit. In 1512 licensing of physicians within four miles of London was put in the hands of the Bishop of London and his officers aided by four Doctors of Medicine. Outside London, licensing was entrusted to diocesan bishops. All save medical graduates had to obtain licenses under penalty of fine. Ambitious in purpose, the law had little effect, and in 1518 Henry VIII chartered the London or Royal College of Physicians with authority to license physicians within a 7-mile radius of London. Five years later another act both confirmed the College's rights within London and extended its jurisdiction to the whole of England. But the extension of the College's authority proved impractical. Lacking administrative machinery outside London, the College had to resort to a variety of ad hoc enforcement techniques which were sometimes undignified and always ineffective. Even within the metropolis, prevention of unlicensed medical practice was a difficult task. With the incorporation of the Barber–Surgeons Company in 1540 and the separation of the apothecaries from their traditional

2

guild affiliation with the grocers in 1617, these "inferior" orders were in position to wage legal battles, if need be, in defense of their medical practice.[2]

The College had occasional success when it took apothecaries and surgeons to court for practicing medicine, but more often it met with humiliation, a humiliation eminently deserved. There never had been enough physicians to deal with the medical needs of Londoners, an inadequacy only accentuated by the influx of vagrants into London brought on by enclosure and attendant rural depopulation in the mid-sixteenth century. Further, the increasing use of printing presses permitted the easy circulation of Arab and Greek treatises on medicine and thus reduced the necessity for specialization. Deprived of its scientific justification and undermined by social conditions, the principle of separation had more shadow than substance by 1600. In this respect the celebrated Rose case of 1703, in which the House of Lords acquitted a London apothecary charged with practicing medicine, simply ratified the practice of the preceding century and a half.

The emergence of a pattern of general practice on the part of surgeons and apothecaries did not eliminate the need for still another kind of healer, the domestic or part-time practitioner. Even by 1620 there was perhaps only one apothecary per 2,000 townsmen in provincial England, and the proportion of physicians to population was, of course, much smaller.[3] Apothecaries, moreover, did not go over to full-time medical practice for another century and a half.[4] In the early seventeenth century they still spread themselves thin, engaging in a wide variety of merchandise including coffee, tea, silk, and chocolate as well as exotic drugs. Deprived of adequate medical care within the profession, many poorer people still sought advice from domestic practitioners—wise women, ministers, farriers, and others with local reputations of medical skill. Although these individuals are often dismissed as "quacks," the word should be

2. *Statutes of the Realm,* 3 Henry VIII, ch. 11; 14 and 15 Henry VIII, ch. 5; 32 Henry VIII, ch. 40; W. S. C. Copeman, *Doctors and Disease in Tudor Times* (London, 1960), pp. 37–38.

3. R. S. Roberts, "The Apothecary in the 17th Century," *Pharm. J., 108* (Nov. 24, 1962), 505.

4. Joseph F. Kett, "Provincial Medical Practice in England, 1730–1815," *J. Hist. Med., 19* (Jan. 1964), 20–24.

reserved for peripatetic mountebanks who set up stages and gave theatrical entertainments as a means of selling their nostrums. Domestic practitioners were, in contrast, sincere villagers making the best of a difficult situation. They flourished also in London, as is manifested by attempts of the surgeons, "minding only their own lucres," to prosecute them. To clarify the legal status of domestic practitioners, a 1542 statute exempted from the penalties on un-licensed practice "divers honest persons, as well men as women, whom God hath endowed with the knowledge of the nature, kind and operation of certain herbs, roots and water and the using and ad-ministering of them to such as be pained with customable disease." [5]

Only occasional attempts were later made to harass domestic prac-titioners. Physicians, who had the greatest influence on medical legislation, were more disturbed by the pretensions of London apothecaries who styled themselves "doctors" than by the activities of part-time practitioners. There was, of course, nothing to stop the grossly superstitious from consulting the grossly superstitious. That this would frequently occur was assumed in law and tolerated in practice, perhaps wisely since superstition can never be legally proscribed.

Toleration, however, was more than an expedient. Medicine was considered not only a science but a "cunning" whose possession was not confined to the formally educated. Cures, in addition, were thought to be as much the work of God as man, and not all had forgotten the dictum quoted by Chaucer, *ubi tres medici, duo athei.* A clear line between the scientific and empirical practitioner did not exist. Physicians still studied the ancillary "sciences" of astrology and alchemy and often prescribed bizarre and dangerous compounds on the supposition that in time of sickness any change could only be for the better.

A survey of English medicine in 1600 would reveal a very large body of town and village people who treated their neighbors with locally grown herbs; a somewhat smaller group of surgeons and apothecaries who at times had episcopal licenses to practice physic, but, even when they did not, prescribed for the middling classes of artisans and yeomen; a smaller group of graduate physicians resident

5. *Statutes of the Realm,* 34 and 35 Henry VIII, ch. 8.

in the provinces, who usually had episcopal licenses or were extra-licentiates of the Royal College; and a very small but well-organized group of consultant physicians resident in London and distinguished by their medical education, elaborate dress, and courtly manners.[6] Appellations like surgeon and apothecary were not accurate indices to functions; the trend was toward general practice regardless of nomenclature. The resultant crazy-quilt pattern has often been assailed for rigidity but was in fact most notable for flexibility. Some kind of medical treatment was available to nearly all, but all did not have to submit to the same type. The physician who arrived in sartorial splendor, waving his gold-headed cane and spouting Latin aphorisms, was likely to have the same reassuring effect on a gentleman that an experienced village woman would have on her neighbor.

While the numerous medical laws had some effect in raising standards and increasing professional morale, they rarely prevented unlicensed practice. Prestige and confidence, not formal qualification, became the touchstones of success. In the absence of generally accepted standards for distinguishing scientific from empirical practitioners, it fell to the individual to decide whom he could trust. The criteria for instilling confidence did not remain static. With the growing popularity of mineral and exotic herbal remedies after 1650, apothecaries were able to assert their superiority over domestic practitioners. Although the latter flourished until the nineteenth century, they declined in importance. But the superior qualification of apothecaries was determined informally by private judgment, not by legal enactments.

The division of medical practice into branches was suited to a society sufficiently developed to permit specialization. It was less firmly rooted in the provinces than in London, had never been strongly ingrained in Scotland, and did not survive the shock of transplantation to America. Few physicians immigrated to America and those who did soon found it necessary to practice all branches. The most common sort of full-time practitioner in the colonies was the surgeon–apothecary who had served an apprenticeship in England and perhaps seen service in the Royal Navy or on the ships of

6. For a discussion and listing of provincial physicians, see John H. Raach, *A Directory of English Country Physicians, 1603–1643* (London, 1962), pp. 7–16.

one of the joint-stock companies. These practitioners began to call themselves physicians, but the absence of guilds and medical societies prevented the development of professional solidarity. Frontier conditions, in any case, were not conducive to full-time practice; a scattered population could not provide enough business to sustain a physician. The experience of many surgeon–apothecaries was similar to that of Giles Firmin of Massachusetts who wrote to Governor John Winthrop, "I am strongly sett upon to studye Divinitie; my studyes else must be lost: for Physick is but a meane helpe." [7]

Domestic medicine became dominant in this situation. A list of prominent Massachusetts colonists who occasionally practiced physic would include two presidents of Harvard College, Charles Chauncy and Leonard Hoar; the first minister of Old South Church, Thomas Thacher; Michael Wigglesworth, Anne Hutchinson, and Cotton Mather. Most practitioners, however, obscure ministers and villagers learned in herbal lore, had only local reputations. Their annals are simple and, for the historian, all too short. The church records of Roxbury, Massachusetts, for November 27, 1665, report that Mrs. Sarah Alcock was "very skilled in phisick and chirurgery" and her "works praise her within the gates." In 1663 Rehoboth carried out what amounted to a raid on Plymouth when it invited Mrs. Bridget Fuller of the latter town "to dwell among us, to attend to the office of a midwife." [8] At times domestic practitioners had cause to sue for fees, and the court records of these legal squabbles yield a revealing picture of seventeenth-century practice. In 1680 John Wing of Essex County, Massachusetts, deposed that he paid Mary Heall, a widow, "for norsing a negro man Zanckey, the tym of the small pox, 5 li. 10 s.' for potacary's drogs and other Expenses in the tym of his sickness." Mary Heall deposed that she took Zanckey into her house "when he had the small pox coming out all over him." But after a few days she noted that "there was something besides that." Zanckey's owner quickly sent a Doctor Bateller. Though it was thought appropriate to call a doctor when complications developed, the widow

7. Giles Firmin to Winthrop, Oct. 26, 1639, *Winthrop Papers, 4* (Boston, 1944), 164.
8. "Rev. John Eliot's Records of the First Church in Roxbury, Mass.," *Fifth Report of the* [Boston] *Record Commissioners* (Boston, 1880), p. 203; Edward P. Conklin, *Middlesex County and Its People: A History* (2 vols. New York, 1927), *1*, 275. Bridget Fuller, who never came to Rehoboth, was the widow of the distinguished Plymouth physician Samuel Fuller.

Heall was persuaded by the "townsmen of Boston" to take Zanckey again when he fell ill the following March.[9]

A variety of enactments manifested the feeling that domestic practitioners were not considered qualified to treat all types of disease. Colonial legislatures were fairly active in the seventeenth century in licensing selected individuals to practice physic and, more often, surgery. The Connecticut General Court, for example, licensed Thomas Lord in 1652 and Daniel Porter in 1654. Jonas Wood of Huntington was licensed by the New York legislature in 1677. Rhode Island went so far as to create Captain John Cranston of Newport a "Doctor of physsicke and chirrurgery" in 1654. But there was a makeshift quality to these efforts. The scarcity of qualified practitioners not only limited the number of licenses but entailed that licenses often had to be granted to individuals who were not primarily medical men.[10] The conferring of the medical degree on Captain Cranston was dubious in the extreme. It was an established principle of common law that one corporation could not charter another corporation. There had been grave doubts about the charter which the Massachusetts General Court gave to Harvard in 1650, and it followed that the charter colony of Rhode Island was on weak ground in usurping the function of a university it had no right to charter.[11]

The colonial licenses, moreover, did not penalize unlicensed practice; the wording of the acts indicates that the recipients had in fact long been in practice. The goal was to single out certain people with colony-wide reputations for official commendation, to encourage rather than to discourage practice. Colonial licensing laws thus had an inclusive, not an exclusive, meaning and often assumed that medical practice would remain largely in the hands of domestic practitioners. Thus a Massachusetts law of 1649 (re-enacted almost word for word in New York in 1665) ordered that:

9. *Records and Files of the Quarterly Courts of Essex County, Mass., 7, 1678–1680* (Salem, 1919), 395.

10. For example, in 1662 a Mr. Woodstock of Salem was licensed to still "strong water." He was also an apothecary but probably had a still first and, with a ready supply of stimulants at hand, expanded his interest to medicine. *Essex Court Records, 2, 373.*

11. Joseph S. Davis, *Essays in the Early History of American Corporations* (2 vols. Cambridge, Mass., 1917), *1*, 20.

no person or persons whatsoever at any time about the bodye of men, women, or children, for preservation of life or health; as Chirurgeons, Midwives, Physitians or others, presume to exercise, or put forth any act contrary to the known approved Rules of Art, in each Mystery and occupation, nor exercise any force, violence or cruelty upon any, whether young or old, (no not in the most difficult and desparate cases) without the advice and consent of such as are skillful in the same Art, (if such may be had) or at least some of the wisest and gravest then present.[12]

The "presumptuous arrogancy" of those who neglected consultation with the wise, not domestic practice itself, was prohibited.

The tide was running against legislative attempts to establish the principle that some practitioners had superior qualifications. The widening scope of domestic practice forced would-be regular practitioners into part-time practice. Thus a physician was cautioned by a relative in 1685 not to come to Philadelphia or New Jersey, "for I hear of no disease here to cure but some Agues, and cutted legs and fingers, and there is no want of empirics for these already." [13] After two years of practice in Virginia, Adam Cunningham concluded in a similar vein that there was

no way of making money in this country so easy as by merchandizing, this being the occupation they all [i.e., all the doctors] come at, for after having purchas'd a little Stock by their Practice they presently commence [as] Merchants, and so make their Fortune. So that if Doctor Blair, Colonel McKenzie, and many others whom I could name have made their Fortunes in this Country, it is not to be attributed to their practice in Physick but to Traffick.[14]

The blurring of distinctions in status accompanied the merging of functions of regular and empirical practitioners. The line between

12. *Massachusetts Colonial Laws* (Boston, 1878), p. 28.

13. Quoted in Francis R. Packard, *History of Medicine in the United States* (New York, 1931), p. 47.

14. Cunningham to Sir William Cunningham, May 24, 1730, quoted in Whitfield Bell, Jr., "Medical Practice in Colonial America," *Bull. Hist. Med., 31* (Sept.–Oct. 1957), 446.

science and empiricism had not always been sharply drawn in England, but various institutions—guilds, medical societies, and medical schools—permitted discrimination among types of practitioners. Because of the absence of such safeguards for status in America, physicians had to depend almost entirely on winning public approbation to gain distinction. Deprived of institutional protections of their status, medical practitioners expanded their interests to general trade. This in turn left the field open to empirics, whose commanding position further discouraged attempts at full-time practice. By 1720 a chain reaction ensuring the predominance of domestic practice had been touched off. A revealing illustration of this process was recorded by Dr. Alexander Hamilton during his visit to Long Island in 1744. While he was staying at an inn in Huntington, a crowd of "town politicians" tramped in, among whom

> was a fellow with a worsted cap and great black fists. They stiled him doctor. Flat [the innkeeper] told me he had been a shoemaker in town and was a notable fellow att his trade, but happening two years agoe to cure an old woman of a pestilential mortal disease, he thereby acquired the character of a physitian, was applied to from all quarters, and finding the practice of physick a more profitable business than cobling, he laid aside his awls and leather, got himself some gallipots, and instead of cobling of soals, fell to cobling of human bodies.[15]

The situation changed rapidly after 1760. Americans began to travel in large numbers to Scotland where the renown of its medical school was making Edinburgh an intellectual capital of Europe. Young provincials there studied the medical systems of William Cullen and John Brown, journeyed to London to walk the wards of the great hospitals or to breakfast with the learned Quaker physician, John Fothergill, and conceived the desire to establish in America a *beau monde* of medical science akin to Britain's. More than a hundred Americans received the medical degree from Edinburgh before 1800. On returning to America they formed the core of a group dedi-

15. Carl Bridenbaugh, ed., *Gentleman's Progress: The Itinerarium of Dr. Alexander Hamilton, 1744* (Chapel Hill, 1948), p. 91; see also Bell, "Medical Practice in Colonial America," pp. 65–66.

cated to the creation of a well-regulated profession. The first fruit of their labor was the University of Pennsylvania's medical school, chartered in 1765 with a faculty composed entirely of Edinburgh graduates.[16]

By 1780 a medical elite, graduates of Edinburgh or the University of Pennsylvania, existed in the major American cities. Its ranks were swelled by veterans of the Continental Army's medical service, like John Warren of Massachusetts, not graduates but sufficiently distinguished to be awarded high military positions. The characteristics of this elite were twofold—since its members held either medical degrees or titles gained in the war, it could be readily identified; and it was larger than previous elites. Physicians like Cadwallader Colden and William Douglass had participated in medical clubs in New York and Boston in the early eighteenth century. But these clubs disintegrated as members died or retired. The new elite, in contrast, was guaranteed an accession of graduates as more medical schools were chartered.

In a recent graduate of Edinburgh, John Morgan of Philadelphia, the elite found its patron and prophet. After serving an apprenticeship under Dr. John Redman of the same city, Morgan left America in 1760 for three years to study in London, Edinburgh, and on the Continent. On his return he played the key role in launching the University of Pennsylvania's medical department, and at the first commencement in 1765 he delivered his celebrated *Discourse*.[17]

Morgan wanted not only medical schools, but good ones, up to the best European standards with adequate clinical facilities and course work embracing the whole of medical science. Instead of passing their impressionable years as apprentices, sweeping floors and marking time in a master's shop, students were to devote themselves to learning Latin, Greek, and French, and acquiring an acquaintance with mathematics and natural science before entering medical school. But Morgan's aim was not to produce a medical jack-of-all-trades, a better-educated version of the physician–surgeon–apothe-

16. Douglas Guthrie, "The Influence of the Leyden School upon Scottish Medicine," *Med. Hist., 3* (April 1959), 120–21.

17. John Morgan, *A Discourse upon the Institution of Medical Schools in America ... with a Preface Containing, amongst other things, the Author's Apology for attempting to introduce the regular mode of practising Physic in Philadelphia* (Philadelphia, 1765).

cary already too common on the American scene. He had been told that to expect to make a living on physic alone was to forget that he was born an American. But he was determined to confine himself to internal medicine, and hoped that other medical graduates would follow suit.

Morgan had less success, however, with his proposal to separate the branches of medicine than with his plans for medical education. The young Benjamin Rush predicted that Morgan's plan to specialize would prevent him from getting much business. Philadelphians were accustomed to paying a comprehensive fee for medical services. Morgan's scheme appeared to double medical charges, with one fee going to the physician for advice and another to the apothecary for drugs. To all who would listen, Morgan argued that under the current system the charge for advice was hidden in the fee for drugs. But suspicion remained and Morgan had to execute a strategic withdrawal. He explained that he did not expect a fee for each visit in a long illness, nor would he charge the poor a retaining fee. He was even willing to leave the fee in part, or wholly, to the patient.[18] But this only made his position more anomalous. An English physician was identified as much by his guinea calling fee as by his dress and education. A doctor who let patients bargain with him over costs was simply not a physician in the traditional sense. Moreover, Morgan overestimated the degree to which specialization was practiced in Britain. In the English provinces and even in Edinburgh the pattern was general practice. Specialization in internal medicine survived only in court circles in London, but Philadelphia had no court and was not to have a court physician.[19]

Morgan's petition to the Proprietors in 1766 to incorporate a medical society in Philadelphia was allied with his plans to separate the branches and establish medical schools. Morgan envisioned a national College of Physicians whose license would be recognized throughout the colonies, but his grandiose scheme was vetoed by Thomas Penn. Similar plans to reassert the long-dormant distinction between scientific and empirical practitioners, however, were in the air. In 1765 Arthur Lee wrote to his brother, Richard Henry Lee:

18. Ibid., pp. xiii–xviii, p. ix.
19. Whitfield Bell, Jr., *John Morgan: Continental Doctor* (Philadelphia, 1965), pp. 129–32.

I was just now thinking that irregular practice for the future might be prevented by a very simple method, that is, by making an Act that for the future every man that settles in a Colony as a Physician, shall, previous to his practice, present his Diploma to the Speaker, or to the Assembly, and receive from them a Certificate, to be registered in the County Court, where he is to practice. That all persons undertaking to order medicine to sick people, without being so qualified shall subject themselves to a prosecution and penalty.[20]

Lee's letter marks a subtle but ominous shift in the meaning of a license. The medical and surgical licenses granted by colonial legislatures were only attestations of fitness. They in no way excluded the unlicensed from practice, as Lee proposed. A healthy respect for the realities of colonial America was being superseded by well-intentioned but visionary agitation for a degree of regulation incompatible with the entrenched position of domestic practice.[21]

Plans such as Lee's, however, began to receive favorable attention. In 1760 the New York legislature, noting the abuses of "many ignorant and unskillful persons in physic and surgery," forbade any person to practice until examined by a committee of colonial officials and prominent physicians. In 1772 New Jersey required that physicians henceforth be examined by a medical board and be licensed by the courts. "As the Benefit of Medical Institutions, formed on liberal principles, and encouraged by the Patronage of the Law, is universally acknowledged," the Massachusetts Medical Society was incorporated in 1781.[22]

Medical legislation gained impetus in the early years of the nineteenth century. In older states such as New York, South Carolina,

20. Arthur Lee to Richard Henry Lee, March 20, 1765, quoted in Bell, "Medical Practice in Colonial America," p. 452.

21. For an illustration of the difficulties of educated physicians in securing patronage even after 1760, see letter of John Watts to Col. Isaac Barré, Nov. 15, 1763, *Letter Book of John Watts, Merchant, and Councillor of New York, January 1, 1762–December 22, 1765* (New York, 1928), p. 198.

22. Charles B. Coventry, "History of Medical Legislation in the State of New York," *New York J. Med., 4* (March 1845), 152; Bell, "Medical Practice in Colonial America," p. 453; Walter L. Burrage, *A History of the Massachusetts Medical Society* (privately printed, 1923), pp. 63–67.

Maryland, New Jersey, and Connecticut, a license could be obtained only by membership in an incorporated medical society or by passing an examination conducted by such a society. Sparsely populated states like Mississippi, Alabama, and Louisiana with poorly organized professions, designated certain physicians as official licensing boards. Unlicensed practitioners were subject to fine and imprisonment, and prohibited from suing for fees. By 1830 thirteen states had passed licensing legislation.[23]

Within the space of little more than a decade, however, nearly every state had repealed its penalties on unlicensed practitioners. Alabama and Ohio led the way in 1833, Mississippi followed in 1834, Georgia and Massachusetts in 1835, Maine in 1837, South Carolina in 1838, Maryland and Vermont in 1839, Connecticut in 1843, and New York in 1844. Licensing laws remained in force until 1852 in Louisiana and were never repealed in New Jersey.[24]

The attempt to distinguish in law between scientific and empirical practitioners was a failure. In 1860 as in 1760 a patient had to rely largely on his own judgment in selecting his physician. To explain this process of repeal of license requirements and its effects, I have selected five states for study—Massachusetts, New York, Maryland, South Carolina, and Ohio. Penalties on unlicensed practice were repealed in all five. Despite this, Massachusetts had considerable success in raising professional morale and inducing physicians to join its medical society; the failure of the other states to achieve this goal provides an interesting contrast. The selected states also afford a reasonable geographical coverage—New England, middle Atlantic and southeast states, and the northwest frontier of that era. The states were not chosen at random but are, in a strict sense, typical. (See Appendix 1.) Issues which arose elsewhere were more pointedly and dramatically played out in these states.[25]

23. Coventry, "History of Medical Legislation in the State of New York," p. 159.
24. Henry B. Shafer, *The American Medical Profession, 1783–1850* (New York, 1936), pp. 208–14.
25. In my doctoral dissertation, on which the present study is based, I included Louisiana. My feeling was that the presence of French and Spanish traditions of firm control over the profession might have offset the disintegrating effects of the New World environment. For a variety of reasons, however, I concluded that Louisiana's regulatory attempts were feebler than those of the eastern states. Within New Orleans this was largely due to incessant animosity between French- and English-speaking physicians. Throughout the rest of the state, difficulties of communication frustrated

American Licensing

The impetus behind the incorporation of the Massachusetts Medical Society on November 1, 1781, came from a group of fourteen Boston physicians whose cooperation was evidence of the degree to which disaffections caused by the Revolutionary War had abated. The older physicians, James Pecker, Samuel Danforth, Thomas Kast, and James Lloyd had sympathized with Britain. Among the younger physicians John Warren, whose brother had died fighting with the patriots at Bunker Hill, had established a reputation at the Continental military hospital as Boston's leading surgeon. The petitioners for incorporation, however, were bound by nonpolitical ties. The oldest was only fifty-seven; the average age a little over thirty-five. Eleven had been graduated from Harvard and all but one were members of the Boston Medical Society founded in the previous year for the exchange of fellowship and information.

The incorporating act limited the number of fellows to seventy, though the society could grant letters testimonial to any practitioner who passed its examination in order that:

> a just discrimination should be made between such as are duly educated and properly qualified for the duties of their profession, and those who may ignorantly and wickedly administer medicine whereby the health and lives of many valuable individuals may be endangered or perhaps lost to the community.[26]

A letter testimonial of the society was not so much a license in the strict sense, a permission to pursue an occupation free from legal penalties, as a recommendation that the holder was competent and fit for public trust. Unlicensed practitioners were not legally penalized, but it was hoped that they would be ostracized by the community. In raising the standard of practice the society relied on judi-

---

even the rudiments of cooperation among physicians. It is reasonable to suppose that the difficulties of rural Louisiana were substantially the same as those of Alabama, Mississippi, and other frontier states. In any event the ruggedness of the environment more than offset the inherited tradition of centralization. See Joseph F. Kett, "Regulation of the Medical Profession in America, 1780–1860," Ph.D. thesis (Harvard University, 1964), pp. 18–22, 39–43, 130–41.

26. *Mass. Special and Private Statutes, 1* (1781), 25.

cious bylaws outlining educational requirements. In 1790, for example, it decided to insist on a knowledge of geometry and natural history as well as three years of study under a reputable practitioner as a preliminary to examination.[27]

The society had the wisdom to confine its licensing efforts to recommending competent practitioners, but the separation of members into fellows and licentiates exemplified the dangers of an overzealous emulation of British institutions. The principle of separate classes was borrowed from the Royal College of Physicians, which was nearly wrecked by bickering between fellows and licentiates in the eighteenth century. Separation rested on two assumptions: that licentiates would be satisfied with their helot status, and that there was such an abundance of qualified physicians seeking entrance that some could be allotted higher position. History and common sense refuted the former assumption, and the character of Massachusetts society negated the latter. In 1781, with only two medical schools in the United States and none in Massachusetts, there were few qualified physicians to draw from. The society's job was to find these few and convince them to join; to act, in other words, as a magnet, not as a winnow. After futilely wooing potential members for twenty years, the society gave up the separation of classes. After 1803 any student who passed its examination and practiced with good repute for three years could become a fellow. The demands of a rapidly expanding American profession thus eliminated in two decades a barrier which had survived in England for more than two centuries.

Though the center of population had moved west since 1781, the medical profession was not organized outside of Boston. Corresponding committees had been established in a number of counties in 1785, but they were concerned only with the communication of useful or remarkable cases. To make the society more appealing to rural practitioners, the 1803 statute empowered the councillors to establish subordinate societies anywhere in the state. These were to be composed of fellows residing outside of Boston and such candidates as they saw fit to license. By 1841 eighteen district societies had been formed, thus adding a dimension of decentralized administration to the affairs of the parent body.[28]

27. Records of the Mass. Med. Soc., April 14, 1790. MSS, library of the Massachusetts Medical Society, Boston.

28. Burrage, *A History of the Massachusetts Medical Society*, ch. 10.

In 1818 and 1819 the voluntary nature of the society was qualified. Practitioners not holding a license from the society or a medical degree from Harvard were forbidden to sue for fees. But the society did not ask for this penalty and was diffident of its effectiveness. In 1835 the prohibition was removed in accordance with the wishes of the greater part of the society because it excited sympathy for unlicensed practitioners without curtailing their activities.[29] In other states the profession heatedly opposed attempts to repeal the fee penalty but was unsuccessful. The different approach of the Massachusetts profession saved it from public humiliation. It was "not so much by the enactment of its laws, as by the high character and honorable conduct of its members" that the society influenced practice.

New York and South Carolina followed the example of Massachusetts in establishing semipublic corporations, but with less wisdom and success. Not until 1797 was an attempt made to regulate practice in New York State, and the statute of that year was stillborn since no provision for enforcement outside of New York City was made.[30] The impetus for more stringent legislation came from rural doctors conscious of the limitations of the 1797 enactment. A medical society had existed in Saratoga County near the end of the eighteenth century. After a period of dissolution it was revived in 1805. Physicians from the adjoining counties of Washington and Montgomery were invited to join, and consultations were begun over ways to elevate the profession. From these discussions came a petition for an effective licensing law. Similar proposals were made by the "Medical Society of the State of New York," a New York county society.[31] The result was passage in 1806 of the most elaborate medical law yet enacted in the United States.

Medical practitioners in each county were authorized to form societies and elect examiners (called censors). No student could be examined until he had studied medicine for three years. A state society, composed of delegates from county societies and authorized

29. *Mass. Gen. Laws*, 1817, ch. 131; 1818, ch. 113; Reginald H. Fitz, *Rise and Fall of the Licensed Physician in Massachusetts, 1781–1860* (reprinted from *Trans. Ass. Amer. Phycns.*, 1894) , p. 12.

30. Coventry, "History of Medical Legislation in the State of New York," p. 153.

31. Minutes, Med. Soc., County N.Y., March 3, 1827. MSS, New York Academy of Medicine; Daniel H. Calhoun, *Professional Lives in America: Structure and Aspiration, 1750–1850* (Cambridge, Mass., 1965) , pp. 28–29.

as a court of appeals for rejected candidates was incorporated. In July 1806, twenty county societies took advantage of the general incorporation provisions of the statute. The penalty for unlicensed practice was a prohibition on suing for fees. But in the following year doctors who practiced only with domestic roots and herbs were exempted, a concession to the paucity of qualified physicians in rural areas.

In Massachusetts the state society preceded the county or district societies; in New York many county societies were in existence first, and the state society was never more than a loose federation. Issues which could be decided through bylaws of the society in Massachusetts became the subject of legislation in New York. As a result, in trying to ensure uniformity among fifty or more county societies, New York legislators passed an excess of laws whose provisions, the historian notes with satisfaction, were often as baffling to contemporaries as to him. The exemption of herbal practitioners from legal penalties was discarded in 1827, reinstated in 1830, partly removed in 1834, and apparently reinstated once again in 1835.[32] An exasperated medical professor conceded in 1845 that the medical law of the state

> is extremely complicated, made up of portions of separate acts passed by different legislatures, the provisions of one act often appearing to conflict with the provisions of a preceding act, so that to a person who has not watched the successive changes, it is difficult, if not impossible, to understand the provisions of the present law.[33]

For Massachusetts the problem was to create a requisite number of district agencies; for New York the difficulty lay in establishing uniformity amid a plethora of local agencies.

In 1789 the Medical Society of South Carolina was founded in Charleston. Prominent among its initiators were David Ramsay, the historian of South Carolina and the Revolution, and Peter Fassoux, who served as first president. At its inception the society resembled an eighteenth-century English club. Unincorporated, its main pur-

32. *N.Y. Revised Statutes,* 1827, pt. I, ch. 14; *N.Y. Laws,* 53 sess. (1830) , ch. 126; 57 sess. (1834) , ch. 68; 58 sess. (1835) , ch. 35. Coventry, "History of Medical Legislation in the State of New York," p. 157.
33. Coventry, p. 151.

pose was the exchange of medical information and good fellowship. Suitably for the latter goal, its meetings were held in the "Southwest Room in the City Tavern." Members were to furnish in rotation dissertations on some medical case or question. A few rural practitioners were admitted in the early years, but in 1794 it was found necessary to exempt them from the quarterly dues. Being too far removed from Charleston to use the society's small library, they had little incentive to keep up membership. By 1793 the society was sufficiently established to seek incorporation for the usual purpose of holding land, and, "after the custom of other well regulated Kingdoms and States," to organize a College of Physicians with licensing authority. But the Medical Society of South Carolina could not yet claim to be a state medical society. While incorporation was granted, licensing power was withheld. After 1793 the society confined itself to making public-health recommendations to the city council, but these were generally ignored.[34]

The absence of licensing authority was a vexation. In 1808 David Ramsay noted:

> Clergymen and lawyers, before they are authorised to exercise their respective functions, are examined and licensed by competent judges; but the practice of physic is free to every man or woman who chooses to undertake it.[35]

A change in attitude came in 1817. The Medical Society of South Carolina became a licensing board for the eastern half of the state, while thirty western physicians were formed into a second board at Columbia.[36] Unlicensed practitioners were forbidden to sue for fees and were subject to fine and imprisonment, but membership in the society was not mandatory. Rural physicians were still reluctant to join, and district societies were not formed until much later. The Columbia board dragged on a feeble existence and apparently was

34. Minutes, Med. Soc., S.C., July 28, 1792; Dec. 24, 1789; June 28, 1794; Nov. 30, 1793; May 1, 1795. MSS, library of Medical College of South Carolina.

35. David Ramsay, *The History of South Carolina from its First Settlement in 1670 to the Year 1808* (2 vols. Charleston, 1809), 2, 114.

36. *S.C. Statutes at Large*, no. 2139; Joseph I. Waring, *A History of Medicine in South Carolina, 1670–1825* (Charleston, 1964), p. 160. Medical degrees were recognized as valid for practice, but Waring is mistaken in claiming that two years of apprenticeship entitled a candidate to a license without examination. The wording of the act makes it clear that apprenticeship was only a preliminary to examination.

disbanded before 1830. Continued preponderance of the low counties was to characterize South Carolina's medical history prior to 1860.

Maryland displayed both a readiness to charter a medical society and qualms about the monopolistic tendency of incorporation. In 1799, 101 practitioners representing all of Maryland's nineteen counties were incorporated as the Medical and Chirurgical Faculty of Maryland. The legislature authorized the Faculty to appoint a Medical Board of Examiners composed of seven practitioners from the Western Shore and five from the Eastern Shore to certify candidates for practice either after examination or upon the production of a diploma from some respectable college. A fine of fifty dollars and a prohibition on suing for fees was imposed on unlicensed practitioners and periodically re-enacted. Licentiates did not have to join the Faculty and for a time they were actually discouraged from joining. Signs of hostility from the legislature forced a more tolerant posture on the Faculty. After 1807 it sanctioned the creation of district societies which, like the parent society, followed generally inclusive membership policies.[37]

The early licensing history of Ohio contained some elements similar to those of the preceding states and other elements pertinent to its frontier character. Ohio's remarkable growth between 1803 and 1850 posed special problems for its medical profession, problems which made it difficult for the government to pursue a consistent regulatory policy. Since few of the early Ohio practitioners had medical degrees, the legislature had to work with a group of military surgeons and some self-styled doctors who had at best served an apprenticeship.[38] As in many frontier states, there was no identifiable hierarchy of eminent physicians during the first quarter of the century. Cincinnati, rapidly assuming preeminence among cities of the Ohio Valley, might have provided leadership, but its medical profession was notoriously ridden with factionalism. The result was that the primary impetus to professional organization had to come from the state legislature, not from within the profession.

Between 1811 and 1824 Ohio enacted no fewer than seven regula-

37. Eugene F. Cordell, *The Medical Annals of Maryland, 1799–1899* (Baltimore, 1903), pp. 42, 54, 70, 92; *Laws of Maryland*, 1798 sess., ch. 105.
38. Frederick C. Waite, "The Professional Education of Pioneer Ohio Physicians," *Ohio State Archaeol. Hist. Q., 48* (1939), 189–97.

tory laws. Where other states incorporated existing private societies, Ohio had to create the societies and designate their membership in the first instance. The creation of a number of district societies only intensified the problem of ensuring uniform procedures and admissions standards, but the legislature attacked the problem by forcing the district societies to send delegates to periodic state medical conventions. Ohio regulated, among other things, the size of penalties on unlicensed practice, the dates on which district societies could meet, and the composition of boards of censors in each district. The legislature acted as a kind of schoolmaster toward the district societies, even charging them with the publication of scientific papers. Instead of discouraging regulatory efforts, frontier conditions and an unsettled society had the opposite effect in Ohio.[39]

By 1830 the foundation for regulation of the profession had been completed in the five states. New York alone continued to enact legislation, but its efforts were mainly an exhibition of artful dodging. The legislative confusion in New York was due not only to the need to ensure uniformity among county societies but to a change in domestic practice. The herbal practitioners of the eighteenth century were being displaced by a sect known as Thomsonians. Its founder was a New Hampshire farmer, Samuel Thomson, who developed a system of therapy based on a few herbal stimulants and emetics. He sold patents on it to persons who occasionally treated neighbors gratuitously or for voluntary remuneration. Thomsonianism grew into a crusade in the thirties; Thomsonian journals were published and patent holders organized into "friendly botanic societies." The sect did not regard itself as an alternative to the orthodox medicine of the schools and textbooks but as the sole defender of true medical principles. In the late thirties certain members of the botanic societies were deputed to practice generally, and thus became "regular" or full-time practitioners. But established physicians branded them as "irregular" practitioners for their lack of formal education.

The New York legislature responded to Thomsonians in 1827 by forbidding them to sue for fees and making all unlicensed practice

<hr/>

39. The best summary of Ohio licensing laws is in Donald D. Shira, "The Legal Requirements for Medical Practice—An Attempt to Regulate by Law and the Purpose Behind the Movement," *Ohio State Archaeol. Hist. Q.*, 48 (1939), 181–88; see also *Acts of Ohio*, 10 ass. (1811), ch. 25; 11 ass. (1812), ch. 13. Originally the annual conventions were to appoint censors, but after 1813 this was done by the state.

a misdemeanor subject to fine and imprisonment. The Thomsonians, however, were able to secure repeal in 1834 of all penalties except the prohibition against suing for fees. This was substantially the
situation until 1844 when a great medical petition was drawn up by
Thomsonians. Reputedly 31 yards long, it was carried into the Assembly chamber in a wheelbarrow by Samuel Thomson's son John.
After a heated debate the prohibition on suing was repealed. While
unlicensed practitioners could still be prosecuted for malpractice, a
distinction between physicians in point of prior qualification was no
longer made.[40]

The most notable aspect of New York's attempt to regulate practice was its ineffectiveness. From 1806 to 1827 and from 1834 to 1844
the only penalty for unlicensed practice was a prohibition on suing
for fees. Even this restriction was more wounding to pride than
pocket. Botanic doctors had only to demand payment in advance or
threaten to refuse future treatment if not paid. "Our existing laws,"
a legislative committee observed in 1841, "will no sooner put down
the advocates of the Thomsonian system, than Canada thistles can
be exterminated in June by cutting down the stalk." Officials claimed
that empiricism was never more rife and that restrictive laws had
never proved a protection against quackery. Though such laws were
founded on principles of sound justice, there was one unanswerable
objection to them:

> It is entirely impossible in this country to enforce them.
> For many years they have been in existence, and yet men
> have practiced under our eyes openly and avowedly in vio-
> lation of them, and in no one instance has the penalty been
> enforced. . . .
>
> The practical operation of these laws was rather favor-
> able to the class of irregular practitioners. The penalty they
> imposed was never regarded, the disability of collecting
> debts afforded a pretext for demanding payment in ad-
> vance, and gave to their demands the character of debts of
> honor. Besides this they put it in the power of the quacks
> to raise a cry of persecution and represent the regular pro-

40. *N.Y. Revised Statutes*, 1827, pt. I, ch. 14; *N.Y. Laws*, 57 sess. (1834) , ch. 68; 67
sess. (1845) , ch. 275.

fession as greedy monopolists, and thus excite some feeling in their favor among weak and credulous people.[41]

The experience of Maryland and South Carolina was similar to that of New York. In Maryland the Baltimore censors lamented in 1811 the difficulties they experienced in bringing defaulters to justice or in preventing them from committing outrages on uninformed citizens. Magistrates refused to convict unlicensed practitioners, and the examining boards, for want of anything better to do, began to turn from professional to purely scientific concerns. Candidates were occasionally denied licenses, but the only practical way to keep them from practicing was to publish their names.[42] To judge from the activities and success of the Thomsonians in Maryland, however, many people preferred to patronize irregular practitioners, thus negating the effect of blacklisting. In the thirties Thomsonians began to call for repeal of the 1799 law. Agitation mounted until 1839 when hundreds of petitions for repeal from nearly every county were presented to the legislature. A bill allowing Thomsonians to sue for fees was debated at a number of sessions and amended to extend permission to every citizen of the state. On March 29, 1839, the House of Delegates passed the amended version by a vote of 40 to 23. That the House simply forgot to repeal the fifty-dollar fine imposed by the 1799 law, despite its plain intention of throwing medical practice open to all, is evidence of the law's unenforceability.[43]

In South Carolina a physician had to concede in 1838 that the 1817 statute, "in effect, stands already repealed. The Thomsonians are practicing throughout the State with the most perfect freedom."[44] With public opinion on the side of the Thomsonians, successful prosecution of unlicensed practitioners was impossible. In

41. "Report of a committee of the Albany Medical Society," *Trans. Med. Soc. State N.Y.*, 6 (1844–46), appendix for 1844, 57.

42. Cordell, *Medical Annals of Maryland*, pp. 66, 77.

43. *J. Proc. House of Delegates*, Dec. 1838 sess., pp. 35, 42, 57–58, 90–91, 148, 173; *Laws of Maryland*, Dec. 1838 sess., ch. 281. Everyone interpreted the law as removing all penalties on unlicensed practice; there was never any suspicion that the fines imposed by the 1799 act and later re-enacted were still in force. Though the body of the act exempted all citizens from penalties, the title applied only to Thomsonians. This was simply legislative oversight.

44. Quoted in *So. Bot. J.*, 2 (May 26, 1838), 99.

1835 the Medical Society of South Carolina brought legal action against four unlicensed druggists in Charleston, including D.F. Nardin, the editor of the *Southern Botanic Journal* and, until his death in 1838, the leading figure in South Carolina Thomsonianism. To the society's surprise no plea was urged in extenuation, "a prosecution being rather solicited than objected to on their part." Nardin's confidence was amply justified by the grand jury's action in returning no bill against the accused and, by way of expressing their unanimity of sentiment as well as their objection to the course pursued by the society, requesting that their decision be recorded by the court. The society had to acknowledge its defeat by this "most formidable blow which has ever been levelled against the interests of Medical Science in this State." [45]

The society's failure to convict Thomsonian druggists was more discouraging in view of the virtual impossibility of proving that Thomsonian physicians collected fees. In 1835 a committee conceded in reference to the latter that in no instance had it discovered that these practitioners had ever charged their patients in Charleston. If a case could not be sustained against druggists who were paid over the counter in crowded stores, one could hardly be carried against physicians.

The Thomsonians thought little of the prohibition on fee collecting and less of the law's threats of fine and imprisonment. Though the law did the profession more damage than good, physicians continued to oppose repeal. In 1837 the House committee on medical education, composed mainly of licensed physicians, reported unfavorably on a repeal bill. But the tide of opinion was against the profession. The fine and imprisonment penalties were removed in 1838, and the prohibition on suing for fees in 1845.

Ohio had no more success than other states, but her failures were due less to Thomsonian agitation than to difficulty in balancing the needs of local organization and central authority. An 1811 law had divided the state into five districts, without provision for annual general meetings. In the following year the legislature created a state society with provision for district meetings as well as a general meeting. But neither approach ever succeeded. The first meeting of the state society in November 1812 attracted only five delegates, five short

45. Minutes, Med. Soc., S.C., Sept. 15, 1835, and Oct. 12, 1835.

of a quorum. A new effort was made in 1821 when each district society was authorized to send one delegate to a state convention which was, in turn, to establish uniform qualifications for licensure. The conventions, however, could only advise on procedure; examinations remained the prerogative of the district societies. Though five conventions met between 1821 and 1833, each district continued to lay down its own rules governing examinations. Since a license from one district was valid anywhere in the state, a rejected candidate had only to trek from district to district until he found a sympathetic censor.[46]

By 1833 the weakness of the district system was obvious, and the convention of that year petitioned for a state licensing board. It also asked that penalties on unlicensed practitioners be removed since virtually no successful prosecutions had been carried out. The legislature granted the second request but stunned the profession by repealing all laws establishing incorporated district societies. Medical societies in Ohio became purely voluntary and private organizations.[47]

In many respects Massachusetts was more fortunate. The Massachusetts Medical Society opposed severe penalties on unlicensed practitioners and devoted itself to raising professional standards and morale. To judge from contemporary appraisals, it had considerable success. In 1820 John Collins Warren observed that since the society's formation "the profession has assumed a new character in this part of the country. Empiricism is scarcely heard of in some districts; in all it is rapidly diminishing." To make honorable physicians known to each other and to the public was the society's purpose and its achievement. James Jackson, who had been graduated from Harvard a year before Warren and who worked closely with him at the Harvard Medical School and Massachusetts General Hospital, shared his views on the desirability of reliance on voluntarism. The goal of raising medical standards, Jackson asserted, could never be achieved

46. Shira, "Legal Requirements for Medical Practice," p. 185; Robert G. Patterson, "The Role of the 'District' as a Unit in Organized Medicine in Ohio," *Ohio State Archaeol. Hist. Q., 49* (1940), 366–77.

47. "Memorial to the Assembly from a meeting of the general medical Society of Ohio," *J. House of Representatives, State of Ohio,* 31 ass. (1832), p. 27; *West. J. Phys. Med. Sciences,* 7 (Oct. 1, 1834), 480–82; *Thomsonian Recorder, 1* (Dec. 15, 1832), 125, 129.

by positive law in America where people were so zealous of their rights.

The police power of the society, specifically the threat of expulsion, was adequate to bring many recalcitrants into line. In 1846 Dr. Lyman Larkin promised to withdraw his recommendation of Page's Syrup and "to abstain from recommending or selling that article, or any other secret remedies." In 1854 Dr. Charles Calkins was expelled for "culpably procuring abortion." The same penalty was imposed on Dr. Henry Hooke of Lowell for writing for a "notoriously vile and quackish paper called the 'Medical Expositor' " and visiting patients under the care of other physicians. The expelled physicians were unsuccessful "in diverting the confidence of the community from regular physicians to themselves." [48]

A more controversial case began in 1836 with the expulsion of Dr. John S. Bartlett of Marblehead. Bartlett had joined the society in 1833, two years after his graduation from Harvard Medical School. Shortly after joining he became friendly with a Dr. John Williams, an English oculist with a medical degree from Paris. European physicians of varying repute frequently came to America, traveling from city to city but never staying long enough to obtain licenses. The presence of these "transatlantic medicine mongers" rankled medical societies. Prosecution was ineffective because of their peripatetic habits, but Bartlett's consortment with Williams gave the society an opportunity to strike an indirect blow at Williams by disciplining one of its members.

Expulsion carried a denial of consultation rights, a penalty Bartlett conceded was highly injurious to his character and prospects. "Medical gentlemen," he added, "have refused to consult with me, and I have lost prospective practice." Rather than humbly petition for readmission, however, Bartlett challenged the validity of the society's charter on the grounds that it contravened privileges of Harvard medical graduates, especially "the right of consultation without referring to any body of men." [49] The society was sufficiently impressed by his case to buttress its own with an assertion of Williams'

48. Quoted by Fitz, *Licensed Physician in Massachusetts*, p. 9; Records, Mass. Med. Soc., May 27, 1846; May 25, 1854; May 26, 1858.

49. *Report of Evidence in the Case of John Stephen Bartlett, M.D., versus the Mass. Medical Society* (Boston, 1839).

shady character. A hard bargainer, Williams usually demanded fifty to a hundred dollars in advance, forced poor patients to pay a minimum fee, and relied on secret potions to cure blindness. The legislature, unwilling to become involved, confined itself to taking down evidence on both sides. The necessity for a decision was averted by Bartlett's death in 1840.

The cases of Calkins, Larkin, Hooke, and Bartlett involved familiar questions of medical ethics. The impropriety of consulting with charlatans or visiting patients under the care of another physician had been emphasized in the code of ethics formulated in 1796 by an English physician, Thomas Percival, and adopted by many American medical societies. A more difficult question was presented by homoeopathy. Like Thomsonians, homoeopaths had a coherent body of doctrine which stressed that diseases could be cured only by administering small doses of remedies that produced symptoms similar to those of the disease. Unlike Thomsonianism, however, homoeopathy was carried to America by graduates of leading Continental universities. Homoeopaths formed their own medical societies, but they craved acceptance as well by established learned societies.[50]

Confusion characterized the initial reaction to the new sect. To show that no hostility existed against them and because "toleration is the spirit of the age," the *Boston Medical and Surgical Journal* frequently printed communications from homoeopathic physicians. But a different note had been sounded by Oliver Wendell Holmes in "Homoeopathy and Its Kindred Delusions," an address delivered in 1842 when there were some fifteen to twenty homoeopaths in the Massachusetts Medical Society.[51] However unoffending the doctrine might seem, Holmes argued, it had long assumed "so hostile a position with respect to the Medical Profession, that any trouble I, or any other member of that profession, may choose to bestow upon it may be considered merely as a matter of self-defence." Homoeopathy began, he continued,

> with an attempt to show the insignificance of all existing medical knowledge. It not only laid claim to wonderful powers of its own, but it declared the common practice to

50. See chapter 5 below.
51. "Homoeopathic Practitioners," *Boston Med. Surg. J.*, 27 (Nov. 2, 1842), 219–20.

be attended with the most positively injurious effects, that by it acute diseases are aggravated, and chronic diseases rendered incurable.[52]

By the mid-fifties most orthodox physicians had adopted Holmes' viewpoint that to admit practitioners so hostile to accepted modes of treatment to the Massachusetts Medical Society would court disruption. Since homoeopaths were sincere and educated, however, the usual reasons of charlatanism or incompetency could not be put forward as grounds for exclusion. But in 1854 the Suffolk District Medical Society refused to admit an avowed homoeopath because his devotion to an exclusive system had rendered him unfit to practice medicine.[53] A few years previously the Massachusetts Medical Society had resolved that diplomas from homoeopathic colleges did not fulfill its educational requirements. "We cannot say to them [homoeopaths] as we do in our own diplomas to all who become our associates," the society argued, "that they are well skilled in the healing art, and most worthy of the honors and privileges of the society." [54] It was stretching the point to hold that homoeopaths were unskilled because dogmatic, but professional harmony demanded that violence be done to the canons of logic.

The society's attitude was further complicated by its legal position. Membership was voluntary, but membership regulations were included in the statutory code of the Commonwealth. Thus the society had to convince the General Court that in redefining incompetency it was acting in the public interest, not merely in its own. In addition, shortly after the foundation of the Harvard Medical School an agreement had been reached between Harvard and the society that the former's graduates would be admitted without examination by the society's censors. This privilege was extended in 1837 to gradu-

52. Oliver Wendell Holmes, in *Medical Essays: 1842–1882*, vol. 9 in Writings of Oliver Wendell Holmes (Boston, 1891), pp. 39–40.
53. "Qualifications for Admission into the Massachusetts Medical Society," *Boston Med. Surg. J.*, 53 (Oct. 4, 1855), 212–13. In 1851 Dr. Ira Barrows was expelled for "dishonorable conduct," the vending of "several quack medicines," and practicing homoeopathy. Since there were several charges, his expulsion could not be cited as a precedent for expelling all homoeopaths; see Burrage, *A History of the Massachusetts Medical Society*, p. 426.
54. "Report of a committee of the Massachusetts Medical Society on Homoeopathy," *Boston Med. Surg. J.*, 44 (March 5, 1851), 99.

ates of the Berkshire Medical Institution in Springfield, the only other incorporated medical school in the state. As long as these concessions remained in force, graduates later converted to homoeopathy had to be admitted equally with orthodox graduates. But to retract the privileges would penalize all graduates for the sins of a few, and provoke powerful vested interests.

The society's increasing determination to exclude homoeopaths was a response to the latters' growing popularity. In 1856 the Homoeopathic Medical Society was incorporated, with the same prerogatives as the Massachusetts Medical Society. The older society's licensing monopoly was thus ended, but licensing itself was not. A legal distinction between regular and irregular practitioners was still drawn, but homoeopaths were officially classed as regular physicians. Thinking that homoeopaths would be content with their own organization, the Massachusetts Medical Society secured removal of the privileges of Berkshire and Harvard graduates in 1859. But the Homoeopathic Medical Society was still in its infancy; membership did not confer the same prestige as admission to the Massachusetts Medical Society. Faced with exclusion, homoeopaths succeeded in having all mention of the Massachusetts Medical Society stricken from the revision of the Commonwealth's statutes enacted on December 28, 1859.[55]

Historians have assumed that this omission abolished licensing in Massachusetts.[56] But a more likely explanation is that it was intended only as an insult, an expression of legislative disapproval of the society's efforts to exclude and expel homoeopaths. Digests of laws relating to the society were published in 1861 and 1874 as if nothing had happened. In 1860 the society resolved to refuse admission to all homoeopaths, but it was still wary of expelling such members. In

55. The *Revised Statutes* of 1835, ch. 27, contained a few provisions for the procurement of anatomical subjects as well as a compilation of the 1803, 1818, and 1819 laws relating to the society. In the *Revised Statutes*, 1859, ch. 22, only the provisions concerning anatomical subjects were included.

56. Fitz, *Licensed Physician in Massachusetts*, pp. 16–17. Fitz drew his conclusion from J. H. Benton et al., *Medical Freedom* (Boston, 1899), pp. 10–11. Benton was arguing against the establishment of an effective licensing board with coercive power. The tone of his tract is polemical, and he made no effort to find out how the omission was interpreted in the twenty years after 1859. Oscar and Mary F. Handlin, *Commonwealth: A Study of the Role of Government in the American Economy: Massachusetts, 1774-1861* (New York, 1947), p. 224, follow the Fitz–Benton interpretation.

1870 the American Medical Association threatened to exclude delegates from the Massachusetts Medical Society if it did not purge its
homoeopaths. The society responded by appointing a board of trial
which expelled a number of them in 1873, 1875, and 1877, until all
were disposed of. The charge was "dishonorable conduct" arising
from their concurrent membership in the Homoeopathic Medical
Society. Some of the discharged homoeopaths brought an equity suit
against the Massachusetts Medical Society in 1872. Significantly, neither the plaintiffs and the society nor Chief Justice Chapman made
any reference to the 1859 omission. The homoeopaths instead
claimed that the expulsion power rested with the society as a whole,
not with a delegated trial board. Chapman ruled, however, that the
society's charter constituted it a common law court of special jurisdiction whose proceedings were not subject to injunction.[57] Thus the
Commonwealth's intent was that there be two licensing agencies,
orthodox and homoeopathic. Each had corporate privileges to admit
and expel, but neither could coerce membership.

The line between public and private, government and society, had
always been less distinct in Massachusetts than elsewhere. To have
asked a seventeenth-century town meeting whether it was transacting
official or private business would have been to pose an irrelevant
question. Its actions were taken in the interest of the common weal
which admitted no such distinction. In time it became evident that
all freemen could not assemble to discuss problems of mutual concern. Some became deputees, others deputizers. But the commonwealth idea was maintained in the granting of charters. Private associations were readily incorporated and thus made malleable to the
ends of state. In New York, where general incorporation laws were
not enacted until the 1830s, greater significance was placed on the
individual incorporation. The chartering of the county medical societies in 1806 was the subject of heated debate. When it was finally
decided to incorporate them, the occasion was deemed also suitable
for the passage of severe penalties on unlicensed practitioners. The
Massachusetts Medical Society, in contrast, never asked for such
power and, when penalties were enacted in 1818 and 1819, they

57. *Gregg v. Mass. Med. Soc.*, III Mass. Reports, p. 185; see also *Trial of William
Bushnell et al. . . . for Practising Homoeopathy, . . .* (Boston, 1873).

were soon repealed at the society's request. Although slighted by the statutory revision of 1859, the society maintained its partnership with the state throughout the century.

AMERICA AND BRITAIN

The failure of medical institutions in America was part of a more general collapse of imported institutions. The seventeenth and eighteenth centuries had witnessed the failure of numerous institutions transplanted from England—primogeniture, entail, strong family authority, established religion, laws regulating dress—all the apurtenances of a hierarchical society. The physical immensity of the country and the abundance of free land frustrated every attempt to graft European institutions onto American society.

Before too much emphasis is placed on the distinctiveness of America's experience, however, the declension that had settled on many traditional institutions in England at the time of America's colonization should be recognized. To take two examples, the process of enclosure and the ensuing depopulation had disrupted family authority and produced hordes of migrants. The triumph of sectarian Protestantism in the Civil War and the atrophy of the Church of England after the Restoration had led to a waning of the Church's social role.

The medical profession might well be added to the list. The enthusiasm of Thomas Linacre and other English scholars back from northern Italy matched that of American physicians of a later age returning from Edinburgh. Each group had seen a better world and was determined to effect a scientific renaissance in its own nation. The fruit of one was the Royal College of Physicians, of the other an abundance of state and local medical societies loosely modeled on the College. But the fruit soon turned bitter. A recent and persuasive student of the College has concluded that the only function it ever effectively performed was the supervision of public health. Failure far more often than success marked its efforts to stop unlicensed practice, or even to keep the branches separate.[58] The American medical societies, caught in a democratic upheaval within fifty years of their foundation, were publicly humiliated by the revocation of

58. Roberts, "The Personnel and Practice of Medicine in Tudor and Stuart England. Part II. London," p. 222.

their licensing authority. The causes of frustration were remarkably similar in each case. Neither Linacre nor the Americans paid enough attention to the dominant position of domestic practice and folk medicine. Each sought to monopolize medical practice for trained physicians who constituted only a fraction of the total number of medical advisors.

In any age it is difficult to supervise an individual's choice of physician. Particular circumstances—the tradition of domestic practice, a rural society, the dubious value of the humoral pathology of the schools—made state regulation of medicine an especially thankless task in late eighteenth-century America. But to suppose that the entire effort was doomed from the start would be a mistake. An increase of professional morale and a heightening of public respect for the profession were within reach had physicians and legislators entertained more realistic expectations. But in most states a fatuous confidence in the capacity of government to control private choice frustrated these objects. Massachusetts alone recognized that sectarianism was a cardinal feature of American medical as well as religious life and devoted itself to building a broad base of good will for the profession. New York, in contrast, placed its trust in a parade of statutes, ostensibly severe but in practice conflicting and unenforceable. There was an almost inverse proportion between coercion and success.

The collapse of licensing in the 1830s cannot be explained simply by reference to a Jacksonian mentality scornful of institutional restraints. In the military, for example, the Jacksonian period witnessed a tightening of control over the medical corps. "A medical service, with a head, some capacity for supervision, and a basis for planning, came into existence." [59] Yet the picture elsewhere was different. In areas outside the scope of federal regulation the pattern was disorganization and slackened requirements. The causes of this deterioration were partly ideological but to a significant extent they arose also from contradictions within the medical institutions themselves, contradictions that deserve careful study.

59. Leonard D. White, *The Jacksonians: A Study in Administrative History, 1829–1861* (New York, 1954), pp. 500–01.

TWO

A Prolific Source of Discord

The establishment of medical schools is a prolific source of discord in the profession. In this there is nothing remarkable. When a faculty is to be made up, there are in general many candidates, and of course many disappointed men; who harbour a secret feeling of dislike, towards the successful aspirants. Moreover, there are at the present time nearly a hundred medical professors in the United States, and at least a thousand physicians, who in their own and the opinion of their friends, are as well, or better qualified, to fill the professional chairs, as the existing incumbents. These two great classes, of course, stand in a relation to each other, which predisposes them to hostility.

Daniel Drake, Practical Essays on Medical Education and the Medical Profession in the United States, *1832*

GRADUATES AND LICENTIATES

The medical degrees of Oxford and Cambridge had always been licenses to practice. The charter of the Royal College of Physicians explicitly exempted graduates of the two universities from the necessity of obtaining the College's license which could not confer greater prestige than an Oxford or Cambridge degree and was not sought for its own sake. The fellowship of the College, however, was another matter. The title F.R.C.P. placed a physician at the head of his profession. Only a fellow could become physician to the king or be appointed a consultant at one of the major hospitals. Most Oxford and Cambridge graduates intending to practice in London readily submitted to the licentiate examination in order to qualify for the fellowship; the latter in turn was restricted to such graduates. When conflict arose, it was between licentiates and fellows of the College, not between the College and the ancient universities.

A more difficult problem developed in Scotland as medical societies were incorporated on the English model. The seal of the Royal College of Surgeons of Edinburgh was confirmed by James VI in 1606. Although authorized at first to regulate surgery and pharmacy in Edinburgh alone, the College's jurisdiction was extended in 1694 to surrounding areas. Practice in Glasgow was supervised by the Faculty of Physicians and Surgeons of Glasgow, chartered by James VI in 1599 with authority over all branches. When the medical schools of Edinburgh and Glasgow universities were revived in the early eighteenth century, their graduates were confronted by the claims of the licensing corporations to an exclusive right to regulate practice. Since the license did not usually confer greater prestige than the degree, graduates were reluctant to submit to the examinations of the corporations.[1]

Hostility between the universities and regulating corporations came to a climax in 1815. In that year Glasgow instituted the Master of Surgery (C.M.) degree and claimed it a license to practice. But the Faculty of Physicians and Surgeons of Glasgow disputed this with an assertion that it alone could license surgeons within its jurisdiction. The university relied on a Bull of Nicholas V empowering it to grant degrees in theology, canon and civil law, *et quavis alia licita facultate,* a commission broad enough to cover surgery. But the Bull, as the Faculty pointed out, did not specify that the degree was a license. In reply the university challenged the validity of the Faculty's charter.[2] The Lords Ordinary upheld the Faculty. The result was virtually a war between the licensing corporation and the university. The professors were purged from the higher offices of the Faculty. For their part, the professors consistently prevented the Faculty from obtaining a clarification of its charter. Similar conflicts took place elsewhere in Scotland in the early years of the nineteenth century, dividing the profession into supporters of the universities and supporters of the licensing corporations.[3]

1. James Adair Lawrie, *Letters on the Charters of the Scotch Universities and Medical Corporations and Medical Reform in Scotland* (Glasgow, 1856), pp. 9–13. Although the degree conferred greater prestige, licensing examinations were often more rigorous than university examinations.

2. James seems to have made his physician and surgeon a corporation and done it in a letter to Privy Seal!

3. Alexander Duncan, *Memorial of the Faculty of Physicians and Surgeons of Glasgow, 1599–1850* (Glasgow, 1896), pp. 165–70; John Chapman, *The Medical Institutions*

Anomalies abounded even when graduates agreed to obtain licenses. The London Society of Apothecaries admitted Scottish graduates without examination, but not licentiates of the Edinburgh College of Surgeons, though the latter had met stricter requirements. Graduates of the University of London could practice on their diplomas in Edinburgh but Scottish graduates could not. Ironically, the former had to be licensed by the Royal College of Physicians before practicing in London. Irish and Scottish graduates practiced throughout most of England, though they had no legal right to do so. By 1858 there were sixteen medical corporations or universities in Britain claiming the right to license in all or one of the profession's branches.[4]

Unlicensed practitioners, however, suffered only random harassment. The universities could not enforce penalties. The Royal College of Physicians, which could, had no effective authority beyond a seven-mile radius from London. Attempts to rationalize the licensing structure long met with failure because of the conflicting claims of the various graduating and licensing corporations.[5]

At times Britain tried to legislate directly for her American colonies. From 1676 to 1689 and from 1763 to the Revolution the Crown endeavored to reverse its policy of "salutary neglect" by the imposition of detailed political and economic regulations. Neither attempt lasted long enough to permit legislation concerning medicine. But even if Britain's attempts had been successful—if, for example, the Dominion of New England had survived until 1789 instead of 1689—there could not have been a transplantation of licensing agencies. There was nothing to transplant. A system, a plan with provision for enforcement on a national basis, did not exist in Britain. Many Americans, however, who studied in Scotland came into contact with the regulatory societies. When they returned and sought to create a well-regulated profession, they were naturally influenced by their experience. In America as in Britain, private societies were given public functions. Unfortunately, the students

---

of the United Kingdom: A History Exemplifying the Evils of Over-Legislation (London, 1870), p. 23. Despite its title the Faculty of Physicians and Surgeons mainly regulated surgery.

4. Walter Rivington, *The Medical Profession* (Dublin, 1879), p. 100.

5. Chapman, *Medical Institutions*, p. 45, pp. 6–7.

brought with them from Scotland the same confusion about the validity of university degrees as licenses and thus the same tendency to attach licensing authority to the teaching institutions.

NEW YORK

The central figures in New York medical history between 1790 and 1810 were Samuel Bard, David Hosack, Samuel Latham Mitchill, and Nicholas Romayne. The focal point of their activities was the medical department of King's College (Columbia), where Bard had been the first professor of the theory and practice of medicine and the others had been students. All were exceptionally gifted. Bard's senior position was acknowledged by the others. Romayne dedicated his Edinburgh thesis to Bard, and Mitchill later affirmed that Bard had initiated him into the mysteries of chemistry. Mitchill, "a living encyclopedia," had a respectable knowledge of ancient languages, archaeology, geology, mathematics, biology, and even politics, the last carrying him to Congress as a Jeffersonian Republican. Romayne mixed land speculating with physic in an extraordinary career that included a role in the Blount conspiracy. Hosack, less thinly spread than the others, was an able physican and a remarkable surgeon.[6]

Personal interest, however, exerted a stronger pull than scientific bonds. By the late 1780s Romayne was beginning to experience a cramping of his style in the tiny Columbia department where he was then teaching. He persuaded Mitchill and some other physicians to join him in petitioning for incorporation of a new medical school. Bard blocked the plan in New York, but Romayne, "goaded by a strong ambition to excel in whatever he undertook," profited from the vagueness of the early laws concerning the validity of out-of-state diplomas. Without great difficulty he secured recognition from Queen's College (now Rutgers) and, while lecturing in New York, conferred degrees under the authority of this New Jersey school. He

6. Fred B. Rogers, "Nicholas Romayne, 1756–1817: Stormy Petrel of the American Medical Profession," *J. Med. Educ.*, *35* (March 1960), 258–60; Courtney Robert Hall, *A Scientist of the Early Republic: Samuel Latham Mitchill, 1764–1831* (New York, 1934); John B. Langstaff, *Doctor Bard of Hyde Park* (New York, 1942); Christine C. Robbins, *David Hosack, Citizen of New York* (Mem., Amer. Phil. Soc., *62*, Philadelphia, 1964).

readily surpassed the aging Bard's popularity.[7] But his goal remained a medical school in New York City and in 1806, with the firm allegiance of Hosack and Mitchill, Romayne used his position as first president of the newly incorporated Medical Society of the County of New York to urge issuance of a charter for his medical school. To gain support within the profession he suggested that the charter be granted to the entire county society. Romayne's prospects were further enhanced by the lifelong friendship between Hosack and De Witt Clinton, the Republican mayor of New York City. The now dominant Republicans saw in the chartering of a new medical school a way of offsetting Federalist influence at Columbia.[8] Success came in 1806 with the incorporation of the county society as the College of Physicians and Surgeons, headed by Romayne.

The charter was not granted by the legislature but by the "regents of the University of the State of New York." Created in 1784 to supervise the reorganization of King's College as Columbia, the regents were authorized three years later to charter and visit such colleges as they saw fit and to confer degrees on graduates of colleges which they incorporated.[9] It was hoped that these colleges would ultimately be welded into a single state university, but until such time, the University of the State of New York existed only on the statute books.

Since the College of Physicians and Surgeons was not connected with a university, the appointment of professors was vested in the regents. The county society was empowered only to elect officers of the college, and even this right was revoked in 1808 when Romayne, clearly willing to use the county society only insofar as it served his purposes, received from the regents a supplementary charter vesting in the latter body the appointment of officers. The consequence was to render the county society's control over the college "nominal and

7. James Manley, "Annual Address of 1827," *Trans., Med. Soc. State N.Y., 1807–1831* (Albany, 1868), pp. 391–92.

8. Bard had been a loyalist in 1776 and was a Federalist. Hosack was described by his son as "not being a political man." His friendship with Clinton began when both were boys and flourished in later years when each man developed an interest in natural science. See Alexander E. Hosack, *A Memoir of the Late David Hosack, M.D.* (Philadelphia, 1861), pp. 320–21; John Warren [?], *A Letter Addressed to a Republican Member of the House* . . . (Boston, 1812), p. 11. This letter is officially listed as the work of John Warren but was probably written by his son, John Collins Warren.

9. *N.Y. Laws,* 7 sess. (1784), ch. 51; 10 sess. (1787), ch. 82.

nugatory." [10] In the following year the legislature made the degree of Doctor of Medicine bestowed by the regents a license to practice, thus creating a rival to the licensing authority of the county society.[11]

The college was, in addition, an unsupervised rival. Romayne, Mitchill, and Hosack were, in effect, proprietors of the college. The county society had only nominal influence; the regents, located in Albany and entrusted with the visitation of all colleges in the state, were in no position to exert effective control. It was thus impossible to establish uniform requirements for admission to practice.

It had originally been thought that all American colleges would be proprietary. But by 1800 real power in most colleges had been transferred to boards of visitors. A principal cause had been the inability to find eminent men willing to reside in college as tutors. There was neither sufficient emolument nor prestige in teaching liberal arts. But there was considerable financial profit to be derived from medical instruction and its attendant increase in private practice, a profit not eagerly shared with others.

The faculty of the College of Physicians and Surgeons, led by Romayne, Hosack, and Mitchill, had obtained a near monopoly over teaching emoluments. The sole obstacle, Columbia, was soon surmounted. Hosack had been lecturing on botany at Columbia since 1795 and continued even after his appointment to the college's botany chair. By years of painstaking labor he had cultivated the Elgin Botanic Garden, the finest in the country, at his summer home in Hyde Park. But by 1808 he had grown dissatisfied with his career as a botany teacher. "I do not choose," he wrote to Romayne, "to be

10. Minutes, Med. Soc., County N.Y., Dec. 21, 1819. MSS, New York Academy of Medicine. Medical societies played a key role in establishing medical schools in other states also, including South Carolina and Connecticut. In the latter state the creation of the Yale medical school in 1810 was due to cooperation between Yale College and the state medical society.

11. By putting the diplomas granted by the regents on the same footing with the licenses of medical societies, the 1809 act in effect "invited the students to apply to their Professors for *Degrees*," turning away, as the county society saw it, "from the more natural course of obtaining licenses from Medical Societies." The professors had an interest in seeing that most students who applied for degrees received them, since emoluments were not fixed but dependent on the number of students a professor could attract. One could hardly deny the effect of offering a guaranteed license as a reward for enrolling in the college. According to the county society the proportion of graduates to matriculants was "monstrous." See Minutes, Med. Soc., County N.Y., Dec. 21, 1819 and March 5, 1819.

Botanist, or Midwife" to the college.[12] The professorship of surgery was now the apple of his eye, and when John Augustine Smith was elevated from Lecturer to Professor of Surgery at the college in 1808, Hosack heatedly resigned. Smith's qualifications for the chair were dubious. With only an A.B. degree from William and Mary he was easily the least qualified of the original faculty. Hosack's surgical credentials were impressive and his ambition enormous. Moreover, Hosack had run into debt to maintain the botanic garden, and he correctly suspected that Romayne and Mitchill had secretly worked against his plan to have the state purchase the garden. Hosack was, in addition, appalled by the lethargic condition of medical education in New York. Neither the College of Physicians and Surgeons nor Columbia could match the medical school of the University of Pennsylvania in facilities or enrollment. By a combination of the two New York schools Hosack decided that he could at once reinvigorate medical education in the city and repay Romayne and Mitchill for their opposition to state purchase of the botanic garden.[13] Accordingly, Hosack used his influence with Mayor Clinton, who was a regent, to have a number of professors brought into the college from Columbia's medical department in 1811. Romayne withdrew from the college and lectured for a few years under the authority of Rutgers. Bard, now sixty-nine years old, left Columbia to take the presidency of the college. Columbia's medical school, minus its president and half its faculty, rapidly declined and in 1814 was formally absorbed by the College of Physicians and Surgeons. These developments, however, in no way benefited the county society, now more effectively excluded from the college than previously.[14]

Throughout this period the college faculty used a variety of devices to shut off any residual influence the county society had over its affairs.[15] The climax came in 1819 when the county society

12. Quoted in Robbins, *David Hosack*, p. 78.
13. Ibid., pp. 79–83.
14. Byron Stookey, *A History of Colonial Medical Education in the Province of New York, with Its Subsequent Development (1767–1830)* (Springfield, Ill., 1962), ch. 2. A number of Columbia professors—Wright Post, Archibald Bruce, William Hammersley, and James Stringham—refused to accept their appointments to the college. Bruce taught materia medica and mineralogy under Romayne at Rutgers; the others were brought into the college in 1814.
15. These included an interesting attempt by Romayne to strike up an alliance with the state medical society. In 1808 Romayne persuaded the state society to allow the

called for a reorganization of the college, based on the establishment
of a board of trustees including officials of the county society as well
as professors of the college, a scheme which in effect admitted the
county society to the college by the rear entrance. Hosack belonged to
the county society but his faction was in a minority. The majority, led
by John Watts, Peter Tappen, and Stephen Beekman won approval
of the plan by the regents.[16] The regents simply hoped to settle a
quickly degenerating situation, but the reorganization only ensured
that future outbreaks between professors and members of the county
society would be fought within the walls of the college on Barclay
Street where they would do the most harm. The regents were incapable of exercising a restraining hand. As Hosack noted in 1826:

> The regents from their residence at the seat of government,
> their great distance from the city of New-York, the different
> nature of their pursuits, their unceasing occupation in the
> offices of state, . . . disqualify themselves from entering
> into the details of the government of a college one hundred
> and fifty miles distant.

Yet only a strong authority could check the trustees, who were

> naturally ambitious to attain the same places, privileges,
> emoluments, and honours enjoyed by the professors. It is
> impossible, therefore, that under the influence of that am-
> bition, the board of trustees can be dispassionate and im-
> partial judges of the medical attainments and qualifications
> of the pupils of their supposed rivals, the professors,—they
> cannot become passive spectators, and witness the pecuniary
> prosperity, the reputation and emoluments of the profes-

college one delegate at the former's annual convention. In turn the county society,
hitherto allowed two delegates, was restricted to one. In the same year the state society,
probably goaded by Romayne, launched an attack aimed at destroying the position of
the county societies by depriving them of their rights to determine qualifications of
their members and to prosecute irregular doctors. The New York county society predicted that if the state society had its way the county societies would become "but mere
machines for carrying into effect the regulations of the state society." The state society's
demands were rejected by other county societies and never approved by the legislature,
but they were sufficient to sow more seeds of dissension. See Minutes, Med. Soc., County
N.Y., April 25, 1808 and Oct. 3, 1808.

16. James J. Walsh, *History of Medicine in New York* (5 vols. New York, 1919), 2,
421; Minutes, Med. Soc., County N.Y., December 21, 1819.

sors, without the desire of participating in those honours and emoluments.[17]

Though not such a dispassionate spectator himself, Hosack was fundamentally correct in his evaluation of the 1819 reorganization.

During the next four years the trustees launched a series of inquiries into the state of the college and the fee-taking practices of the professors. As a result Hosack and the other professors were forced to petition the regents for another overhauling of the college administration. In 1825 the regents decided to exclude all practitioners of medicine from the board of trustees: there were to be thirteen members, with the president and vice-president of the college serving *ex-officiis,* the remainder nonmedical men appointed by the regents.

The reorganization plan quickly passed the Senate, but opposition was encountered in the House of Assembly. In the eleventh-hour rush of bills before adjournment, no time was found to take action on the plan. Since the regents needed legislative approval, and since no legislation on the plan could be passed for another year, during which time the county society could marshall more support for its plan, the entire faculty of the college resigned in the spring of 1826. The seceders were Hosack, Mitchill, William Macneven, Wright Post, Valentine Mott, and John W. Francis. For the next few years they were to prove the gadflies of the New York profession.

Their first maneuver was to apply for reappointment by the regents, which they hoped would amount to a vindication of their position. They were surprised and annoyed when the regents turned them down. The regents probably hoped to end the dispute once and for all by creating a new faculty, drawn mainly from members of the county society previously excluded from teaching. The seceders then applied to be constituted a medical faculty of Columbia, and, on being refused, turned to Union College. All to no avail. At this juncture they hit upon the plan used many years before by Romayne —to operate a medical school in New York and grant degrees under the authority of Rutgers. There was nothing to prevent this prior to 1827; a diploma from an out-of-state corporation became a license

17. David Hosack, *An Inaugural Address delivered before the Rutgers Medical College* (New York, 1826), pp. 12–14; 113–22; 140–43; passim. Mott later joined the faculty of the college.

on being filed. To check the attempt of Hosack's "hostile band" the county society had to obtain a new licensing law.

The 1827 licensing statute was directed as much against Hosack's faculty as against quackery. The eighteenth section of the law specified that a diploma from an out-of-state college granted to a student at a New York institution was not a license to practice. The twenty-first section forbade a college to install a faculty in any other place than where the charter located the college. Further, degrees conferred by any college in the state were no longer licenses to practice. Degrees bestowed by the regents were licenses, but the regents granted degrees only to graduates of the state's two incorporated medical colleges—the College of Physicians and Surgeons in New York City and its Western District branch at Fairfield. Hosack could not obtain a New York charter, and without one he could not lure students away from the College of Physicians and Surgeons. His alternatives were a renewed campaign to obtain incorporation or repeal of the 1827 law. While never wholly abandoning the former object, he concentrated chiefly on repeal.[18]

The entire law was suited to the needs of the county societies, and nothing less than total repeal would appease Hosack. In 1829 there appeared a *Circular Letter* [19] to the practitioners of the state and a *Memorial* to the legislature calling for repeal of the 1827 statute; 154 signatures were attached to the *Letter,* and an analysis of them is revealing for what it tells of the forces then crystallizing in opposition to effective licensing. Nearly a third of the signatures (46) were those of members of the New York county society and included most of the Rutgers faculty and a larger group under their influence which hoped to advance its own fortunes by the success of Manhattan College (the name which the Rutgers faculty adopted while seeking incorporation in New York).[20] The remaining signatures were those of aspiring young physicians who objected to a provision

18. James Manley, "Annual Address of 1827," *Trans., Med. Soc. State N.Y., 1807–1831* (Albany, 1868), pp. 391–92.

19. *A Circular Letter to the Practitioners of Physic and Surgery in the State of New-York from the Practitioners of Physic and Surgery in the County and City of New-York with a Memorial intended to be submitted to the Legislature of the State of New-York at its next session* (New York, 1829).

20. Minutes, Med. Soc., County N.Y., Jan. 11, 1830; *Circular Letter,* pp. 21–22. Hosack, Mitchill, Mott, Francis, and Macneven signed the *Letter.*

of the 1827 law which forced licentiates to join the county societies. Their signatures as well as those of Hosack's followers indicated that a good deal of the agitation against the county societies was coming from within the profession.

The *Circular Letter* was a vitriolic indictment of the monopoly over medical practice allegedly given to the county societies by the law. According to the *Letter* the act had completely changed the character of the county societies. From being merely voluntary societies, they were now "held up *pro terrore;* their number convened by legal coercion; their funds collected by direct taxation upon novitiates" (pp. 7–8). The sections of the act authorizing the district attorney to bring prosecutions for malpractice were luridly described. But the central point was that the act had created a monopoly over medical practice out of harmony with the spirit of the age which was to emancipate talent, enterprise, and industry from corporate restrictions and to leave the mind "free to exercise its energies, and the public unrestrained from encouraging what it approves" (p. 12).

The *Letter* grew even more vehement on the subject of the medical schools, noting (p. 10) that:

> No member of the profession, in the cities or counties, can teach in any department, with any hope of emolument, while the incorporated colleges have this monopoly. Every member of the profession is, therefore, prohibited from becoming a teacher, however capable, or however emulous of rising in his profession, lest his honours or emoluments should lessen those of the *incorporated professors.*

This was hardly a disinterested appraisal of the law. The law's intention of punishing incompetent practice was conveniently ignored. Further, only a few of the regular physicians, the allies of Hosack, were excluded from teaching. A significant body within the county society, led by John Watts, was enjoying the emoluments from teaching. But now that Hosack was an outsider he found it convenient to overlook this. The talk about the act of defying the spirit of the age must be considered, insofar as it came from Hosack's followers, as pharisaical. Hosack objected to the new faculty of the college, not because it had a monopoly but because he was not one of the monopolists.

By 1827 pandemonium reigned in New York's licensing structure. The causes were both human and institutional. Romayne had set the standard when he courted the county society's support in petitioning for incorporation of the college and then excluding it from any voice in the college's affairs. Hosack and Mitchill acquiesced in Romayne's dealings and must share the blame. On the other hand, in view of the ruthlessness of Watts and the county society in driving Hosack and Mitchill from the college, one suspects that the story would have been the same had Watts been in Romayne's position in 1807. Teaching medicine was a profitable calling and a passport to an increased private practice. Control of the city's only medical school was too lucrative a prize for fair competition.

Despite its good intentions the 1827 law did little to relieve the chaos. Candidates rejected by one society could no longer seek admission to another. Graduates of out-of-state colleges had to meet educational requirements. But other forces were emerging which were to blow away these shreds of stability.

In 1827 there were only two incorporated medical schools in the state, the College of Physicians and Surgeons in New York City and its Western District branch in Fairfield. By 1841 there were five, and the degrees of all five were licenses to practice. Geneva Medical College was incorporated in 1835 over the protests of professors at the Fairfield branch, who saw it as a rival. The success of the Geneva faculty did not prevent the same arguments from being resuscitated against the Albany Medical College's petition for a charter. It was stated that there were already enough medical schools in the state and that the incorporation of the Geneva school had caused a decline in enrollment at the Western District college. If Albany were allowed to have a medical school, its opponents argued, it would not be long before Rochester, and then Buffalo, would also desire one, "till the institutions outnumber your students." But in 1839 committees of the Assembly and Senate rejected these objections and urged incorporation of the college. The Senate committee nearly apologized for recommending another incorporation. It conceded that of thirty medical schools in the country only five or six were flourishing. Nevertheless, it concluded that another medical college could be chartered without catastrophe. In 1841, two years after the incorporation of the Albany school, lectures commenced at the New York University Medical College.[21]

Even before the floodgates were opened to the incorporation of medical schools, the New York County society had renewed its assault on the license-granting privileges of incorporated medical schools. There was a familiar sound to its charges. The practice of letting schools confer degrees after private examination does not, it argued,

> afford any check to favoritism, the influence of consanguinity and pupilage, the recommendations of powerful men, the neglect of duty, and personal animosities, these examinations being conducted in private, and often by interested individuals, whose word alone must be taken as evidence of the qualifications of the candidate.[22]

To remedy these alleged inequities the society proposed that in the future all examinations for licenses and degrees be held in public, with the answers recorded verbatim. All tests were to be conducted by four boards of examiners, one for each two of the eight senatorial districts. Each county society was to be allowed to select at least one member to the new boards.

With these proposals the intrigue within the New York profession reached Byzantine proportions. The plan was, as nearly everyone saw at the time, a poorly disguised scheme for the establishment of a new medical college in the city. The New York County society had gained control of the College of Physicians and Surgeons in 1826, but only few of its members, led by John Watts, were able to share the profits of teaching. The remainder was excluded, and by 1832

21. "Report of the committee on colleges . . . on the petition of the trustees of Geneva College," *Docs. of Ass.*, 58 sess. (1835), *3*, no. 20; "Report of the minority of the committee on medical colleges and societies, opposed to the incorporation of the medical college in Albany," ibid., 60 sess. (1837), no. 172; "Report of the committee on medical societies . . . ," *Sen. Docs.*, 62 sess. (1839), *1*, no. 19; see also *Docs. of Ass.*, 62 sess. (1839), *2*, no. 29; Norwood, *Medical Education in the United States before the Civil War*, pp. 134–35.

22. "Memorial of the Medical Society of the city and county of New-York . . ." *Docs. of Ass.*, 55 sess. (1832), *3*, nos. 249, 244.

the majority of members had no more opportunity to share the fees than in 1819. Once in a position to examine all medical students, these members hoped to expand their role, first to cramming, and finally to securing incorporation.

Protesting the plan, the faculty of the college pinpointed the motive behind it as one to enable "certain young aspirants to burst the bonds by which they consider themselves at present bound and emerge into full blown professors." A similar line of attack was pursued by T. R. Beck, a protégé of Hosack and professor at the Western District college, and by the state society. The latter's support for the college annoyed the county society. In a remonstrance to the legislature it asserted that the state society had been for some time in a "dilapidated condition" and with few exceptions was composed of physicians interested only in the two colleges. But little could be done to save so tactless a scheme. In vetoing it the Assembly concluded that, if put into effect, the plan would entail not only another medical school in the city but possibly the establishment of schools in every county that had a medical society.[23]

Certain considerations remained constant amid the anarchy of the New York profession. Originally a charter was meant to be a cluster of legal privileges bestowed by the state on private citizens to enhance the common weal. But privileges that nearly anyone could obtain ceased to be privileges. The nature of a corporation, however, changed more rapidly than the attitudes of physicians. Despite the loosening of corporate restraints in the thirties, each faction persisted in thinking its rights exclusive and vitriolically assailed interlopers.

Professional jealousy was natural and hardly confined to the early nineteenth century. The main factor was that degrees were licenses. Professional rivalries thus inevitably became rivalries among the numerous licensing agencies. Hostility between medical school and medical society divided the profession on a more personal level. To Daniel Drake, the most influential medical figure in the western states, the license was only a "certificate of inferiority."

A licentiate may be a good physician, and become a great
man, but still there is an original technical difference be-

23. "Report of Mr. Winfield, from the committee on medical societies and medical colleges," ibid., no. 251.

tween him and a graduate, which everyone recognizes; and, as far as testimonials are concerned, he is one, who has not made the attainments which entitle him to a doctorate.[24]

If licensed physicians could not maintain uniform standards, there was little justification for imposing penalties on the unlicensed.

For Drake the solution was to restrict practice to medical graduates, a solution not practical in New York before 1830. Highly qualified physicians tended then as now to flock to the larger cities. In 1830 this meant that rural practice had to be left largely in the hands of licentiates, not graduates. With the virtual explosion in the number of medical schools in the thirties and forties, it was becoming possible to dispense altogether with a separate class of licentiates. But in New York the damage was done prior to 1830, and license laws were repealed before graduation became the *sine qua non* for practice.

MARYLAND

The years 1807 and 1826, vital in the history of New York's profession, were of equal significance for medical education in Maryland. Although this was a temporal coincidence, similar forces were at work in each state. The first state medical society in Maryland, the Medical and Chirurgical Faculty, received its charter in 1799. Within a few years one of its members, John Beale Davidge, a Glasgow graduate and successful Baltimore practitioner, began to call for the establishment of a medical school, and by 1802 he was delivering private lectures on obstetrics and surgery. Davidge's lectures were at first only sparsely attended, but he soon associated with two other physicians—James Cocke, a former pupil of Sir Astley Cooper at Guy's Hospital in London and a graduate of the medical department of the University of Pennsylvania, and John Shaw, a former student at both Edinburgh and Pennsylvania and a poet of some attainments. Late in 1807 the Maryland legislature was induced to incorporate the College of Medicine of Maryland, with Davidge, Shaw, and three others forming the first faculty.

While the college was not strictly proprietary, there was little

24. Daniel Drake, *Practical Essays on Medical Education and the Medical Profession in the United States* (Cincinnati, 1832) , p. 92.

outside supervision. The state Board of Medical Examiners (the Medical and Chirurgical Faculty) and the professors were designated the Board of Regents of the College of Medicine. Two thirds of the regents were not professors, and the nonteaching majority had few incentives to attend to affairs of the college. For the first five years of its existence, survival of the college was in doubt. Lectures had to be given in a hastily converted shack on Fayette Street. During the winter the cadavers were often frozen solid, and the faculty had frequent bouts with pleurisy. Attendance was very low; only five students were graduated at the first commencement in 1810. The flimsiness of uniting the professors and the Board of Medical Examiners on the school's board of regents was clear at the time, but the legislature had few alternatives. The only institution in Maryland to which the college could have been attached was St. John's College at Annapolis, forty miles distant and not a university anyway. That the College of Medicine was to be proprietary in all but appearance was inevitable.

The entire expense of the college at first fell on the professors. There is no evidence that the Medical and Chirurgical Faculty provided any assistance. In 1808 the legislature authorized the first of a number of lotteries to raise money for an adequate building. The cornerstone was laid in 1811, and in 1814 the classic-revival edifice on Lombard Street was ready for occupancy. Meanwhile, however, the legislature had radically altered the college's government and purpose. In 1812 the college was made the medical department of a nonexistent University of Maryland and authorized to annex faculties of law, divinity, and arts and sciences. The original board of regents was supplanted by the "Regents of the University of Maryland" composed of the professors of the several faculties and the provost.

In 1910 Abraham Flexner cited the "foundation early in the nineteenth century at Baltimore of a proprietary school, the so-called medical department of the so-called University of Maryland," as a precedent for the disastrous proliferation of proprietary schools which long ensured the mediocrity, or worse, of American medical practice. Before the 1812 act he wrote, "a college of medicine had been a branch growing out of the living university trunk. This organic connection guaranteed certain standards, modest enough at that time, but destined to a development which medical education could, as experience proved, ill afford to forego." Flexner recognized that with the rapid expansion of the country, educational standards were inevitably lowered. But had medical schools been an integral part of the university system, they would have shared in the general rise in affluence in the latter part of the nineteenth century, and "medical education would have been a part of the entire movement instead of an exception to it." Under the proprietary system, however, medical schools were run as business enterprises (though not usually successful ones), and professors displayed an understandable reluctance to vote money out of their own pockets to endow adequate research facilities.[25]

Flexner was right about the evils of the proprietary system, but he exaggerated the importance of the Maryland school as a precedent and misunderstood the intent of the legislature in 1812. Despite appearances, the University of Maryland was certainly proprietary. Theoretically, state funds were to be distributed among the several faculties by the regents. But since the medical professors were the regents, they could do as they pleased with legislative endowments. To have expected the professors to create potentially rival faculties would have been a counsel of perfection. The Maryland school, however, was by no means the first proprietary medical school. The College of Physicians and Surgeons in New York, despite random harassment by the state regents, was proprietary for much of the nineteenth century. In 1814 it absorbed the Columbia medical department, not the reverse, and the tail continued to wag the dog until the college was made an organic part of Columbia University in 1891. Although Harvard established a medical department in 1783, the school was removed to Boston in 1811 and there remained a law unto itself until the twentieth century.[26] The University of Pennsylvania did not take over the collection of fees from its nominal medical department until 1896. Teaching medicine was looked

25. Abraham Flexner, *Medical Education in the United States and Canada: A Report to the Carnegie Foundation for the Advancement of Learning* (New York, 1910), pp. 5–6.
26. Ibid., p. 8n.; Donald Fleming, *William H. Welch and the Rise of Modern Medicine* (Boston, 1954), p. 4. As late as 1912 "clinical professors in the Harvard Medical School were chosen on the basis of seniority from among themselves by a group of local physicians, having no status in the university, who met at the Tavern Club in Boston."

upon as a profitable calling, partly because of tuition fees but mainly because of a by-product known as "the reflex"—consultation fees obtained by a professor on the recommendation of his former students. As far as the professors were concerned, the fewer questions asked and the less snooping by boards of regents, the better. The "University of Maryland" was not a precedent but a phase of a much larger movement.

The last thing the Maryland legislature desired, moreover, was to create a proprietary medical school. As early as 1784 it had sought to fashion a university out of unpromising materials by uniting St. John's College at Annapolis on the Western Shore and Washington College at Chestertown on the Eastern Shore into a University of Maryland. But only two convocations of the faculties were ever held, and in 1805 the legislature withdrew its support. When the legislature was considering the petition in 1807 to charter the College of Medicine, an amendment was proposed making the college a medical department of St. Mary's College, a Roman Catholic institution in Baltimore which aspired to university status. Although St. Mary's was not destined to develop more than a theological faculty, the legislature's concern was indicative of its qualms over allowing an unsupervised medical school to grant degrees. The 1812 act was still another and almost desperate attempt to provide a degree of state control over higher education. Later in the century the medical department was made a nominal branch of St. John's College, but neither this nor the pounding of the Hopkins tiger at the gates was to make Maryland's school more than a fair specimen of a generally wretched species.

The evils of the proprietary arrangement were not immediately apparent. The War of 1812 and the subsequent financial panic in 1819 disrupted the economic and cultural life of the city. The machinations of the medical professors did not attract much attention until the 1820s. Friction developed between Davidge and Elisha DeButts on one side and Granville S. Pattison, professor of surgery, on the other. Pattison was a Scot, a brilliant lecturer and the most controversial figure on the staff. He had had a brief and stormy career in Philadelphia before coming to Baltimore. Although he served the university well, especially in developing clinical facilities, he also engendered hostility. He had wrested the surgery professorship from Davidge on arriving in Baltimore, and local physicians were jealous of his rapid rise to eminence on the faculty. The practice of Davidge and DeButts of giving private extramural lectures brought latent antagonisms to the surface. Pattison objected and convened the board of regents which ruled that a professor could lecture only *ex cathedra* during the term. Davidge and DeButts sought redress from the legislature and in 1826 secured confiscation of the university by the state. The functions of the board of regents were taken over by a new board of trustees composed of twenty-one leaders of Maryland cultural and social life, few of them medical men. The proprietary nature of the University of Maryland was, for a time, effectively ended.[27]

The ease with which two dissident professors obtained such a radical change in the university's structure requires explanation. Since there are few surviving records relating to the takeover, most accounts have been based on a polemical pamphlet by Nathaniel Potter, the professor of the practice of medicine, who viewed the confiscation as a plain case of rape. In fact, however, both interested and disinterested factors played a role.[28]

Long before the Medical and Chirurgical Faculty had contemplated setting up a medical school, the state had sought to establish a university. But by 1826 the intent of the 1812 law had been clearly frustrated. As of 1822, nearly $100,000 had been raised by lottery or loaned to the university, but no money had found its way to any faculty save medicine.[29] Only a few lectures had ever been delivered in the theological faculty, and those few mainly to medical students. None at all had been given in arts and sciences. But no faculty was more resentful of the privileged position of the medical professors than that of law. A legal chair had been established in 1823, but lectures had to be delivered in the office of the professor, David Hoffman the noted jurist. A number of prominent Baltimore lawyers, moreover—Nathaniel Williams, William Frick, Upton S. Heath, Roger B. Taney, George Winchester, and Jonathan Meredith

27. George H. Callcott, *A History of the University of Maryland* (Baltimore, 1966), pp. 41–42, 50–52, 55–56; *Laws of Maryland*, Dec. 1825 sess., ch. 190.
28. Nathaniel Potter, *Some Account of the Rise and Progress of the University of Maryland* (Baltimore, 1838).
29. See the "Report of the joint committee to look into the condition of the university," *Baltimore American and Commercial Advertiser*, March 1, 1826.

—held appointments in the university corresponding roughly to the position of lecturer. They probably hoped that confiscation by the state would lead to the establishment of a suitable law building and five or six law professorships, and were ready to unite with Davidge and DeButts to enhance their positions in the university. A legal department was not effectively started until 1869, but Frick, Taney, and Williams were appointed trustees by the 1826 act.[30]

The trustees had, in addition, political and social connections which far surpassed those of the medical professors. The diary of Robert Gilmor, appointed a trustee in 1826, gives a revealing glimpse of the Baltimore elite. Gilmor was president of the Library Company, president of the Maryland Academy of Arts, Sciences, and Belles Lettres, and an official of nearly every Baltimore cultural institution of note. His colleagues and dinner companions included David Hoffman, the law professor, William Frick, the trustee, Peter Cruse and John Pendleton Kennedy, both noted authors and nominal professors in the inactive arts and sciences faculty, and Jules Ducatel, an apothecary and chemist who was later appointed by the trustees to the medical faculty's chemistry chair. Gilmor was also on close terms with Isaac McKim, a leading merchant and capitalist, and Benjamin C. Howard, the son of Colonel John Eager Howard, the Revolutionary hero and probably the most famous person in Baltimore. Both Howards and McKim played leading roles in the launching of the Baltimore and Ohio Railroad in 1827, and all were appointed trustees in 1826.

The trustees on assuming control gave the medical professors fifteen days to apply for reappointment. The professors had little choice. The normally irresistible bait of going forth and starting a new college could not for once be taken, for at about the same time that the confiscation was authorized the legislature chartered Washington Medical College as a rival to the university. The leading spirit in this school was Horatio G. Jameson, a graduate of the University of Maryland (1813) and for long a foe of the medical professors. Had the professors withdrawn, the trustees would have

30. A serious attempt to launch a liberal arts faculty was made in 1830 but did not succeed; see the *Address of the Trustees of the University of Maryland to the Public* (Baltimore, 1830). Partly out of conviction about the inviolability of charter rights and, perhaps, partly out of fear of the appearance of rival professors, Hoffman opposed the confiscation.

appointed a new medical faculty, and thus there would have been three medical schools in a city that could scarcely support one.

The most notable casualty of the confiscation was Pattison, who heatedly resigned and took a position at the University of London. Death depleted the ranks of the faculty in ensuing years, but new professors entered the school, including the prolific Robley Dunglison from the University of Virginia, Nathan Ryno Smith from Jefferson Medical College, and Eli Geddings from the Medical College of South Carolina. But personnel changes did not produce harmony. In 1827 the trustees summarily abolished the graduation fee, hitherto a valuable source of professorial income, on the grounds that the professors might not be so eager to award degrees if they did not stand to reap a profit on every successful candidate. When the university was taken over in 1826, in addition, the trustees seized the infirmary, which had been erected by the professors at their own expense, and forced the professors to attend gratis. The professors protested and were able to secure a settlement of about $15,000 from the trustees. More problems arose over the appointment by the trustees of Henry W. Baxley as anatomy demonstrator. Disliked both by his colleagues and students, Baxley kept the university in a state of turmoil in the early thirties. While it is difficult to accept all of Professor Potter's charges about the maladministration of the trustees, their officiousness cannot be doubted.[31]

The trustees, however, were more than bulls in the china shop. Their determination to keep control of the institution had assumed an unmistakably political coloring with the election of 1828. In that year one of the most influential trustees, William Frick, united with Upton S. Heath, the law lecturer, and Roger B. Taney, then a trustee and later Chief Justice of the United States, to form the Jacksonian party in Baltimore. By 1830 the board of trustees was dominated by an active Jacksonian majority. There were no more stalwart apologists for the board than Nathaniel Williams and John Nelson, both Jackson men. Among the Jacksonian trustees were, in addition, Isaac McKim, the capitalist, Benedict Semmes, who served as a Democrat in Congress from 1829 to 1833, and William H. Marriott. Professor Potter spoke of a virtuous minority on the board,

31. Callcott, *A History of the University of Maryland*, pp. 66-67, 78–79; Potter, *Some Account of the Rise and Progress of the University of Maryland*, pp. 28ff. Davidge died in 1829 and DeButts in 1831.

"literary men always disposed to consult the interests of the school," in contrast to the majority, "illiterate and conceited, inflated with their own importance, and mere calculators of dollars and cents."[32] Since Potter identified the minority as led by three judges of the state's judicial districts, he probably had in mind Ezekiel Chambers, who in 1834 became chief justice of the second circuit, Stevenson Archer, appointed chief justice of the sixth circuit in 1824, and Thomas Beale Dorsey, appointed chief justice of the first circuit in 1824. But before accepting Potter's characterization of the dispute as one between literary men and countinghouse men, the fact that professional men were found on both sides should be noted. A more plausible explanation is that a predominantly Jacksonian majority on the board of trustees was bent on maintaining its party's control of the university.[33]

A series of events in 1837 and 1838 brought party lines into still sharper focus. The medical professors continued to find ample grounds for complaint in the trustees' actions. They contrasted their own frugal management of the infirmary with the spendthrift policies of the trustees. One of the trustees, Solomon Etting, with McKim a co-founder of the Baltimore and Ohio Railroad, seems to have viewed the infirmary as a fief, having himself successively appointed chairman of the infirmary committee at $200 a year, "superintendent" at $400, and "governor" at $800. Etting's control was absolute; patients were admitted and discharged and medicines purchased at his direction. When a minority of trustees, "true friends of the school" according to Potter, protested, the majority resolved that absence from four successive meetings vacated a board seat. When it was noticed that the three judges had missed three consecutive meetings, the majority called for a fourth meeting on a day when the judges had to sit in court, and thus eliminated them from the board.[34]

32. Potter, *Some Account of the Rise and Progress of the University of Maryland*, pp. 35–36.

33. The only prominent Whigs on the board were Ezekiel Chambers and the noted lawyer Reverdy Johnson. The latter's involvement in national politics made him one of the less active members of the board.

34. Eugene F. Cordell, *Historical Sketch of the University of Maryland School of Medicine (1807–1890)* . . . (Baltimore, 1891), pp. 84–85. There were other minor issues between the trustees and the faculty; see Callcott, *A History of the University of Maryland*, pp. 67–68.

The final blow came when the trustees appointed Dr. Baxley, the anatomy demonstrator, to the anatomy chair despite the professors' preference for another. The professors nullified the election and to sustain their action declared the 1826 act unconstitutional. The "Regents of the University of Maryland," dormant since 1826, were revived. Professors Potter and R. W. Hall resigned as members of the trustees' faculty and formed the nucleus of the new regents' faculty. The medical professors with the exception of Baxley then began to deliver lectures under the regents' (i.e. their own) auspices at a local hotel. The trustees appointed a new faculty made up of undistinguished Baltimore physicians. Neither school exactly flourished. The trustees' faculty had to confront an array of nearly empty benches; the regents' lectures were ignominiously terminated when the hotel's proprietor decided to abolish the old building.

Both sides, meanwhile, began legal action. The trustees retained an impressive staff of lawyers led by Roger B. Taney and Reverdy Johnson.[35] The regents countered with the finest Whig lawyer in the nation, Daniel Webster. A lower court decision favored the trustees, but in 1838 the Maryland Court of Appeals overturned the decision and upheld the regents. In 1819 John Marshall had concluded in the Dartmouth College case that an act of incorporation was a contract within the meaning of the Constitution. Webster, who had defended Dartmouth College, now put forward similar arguments and was sustained by Chief Justice Buchanan. Buchanan reasoned that the 1826 act was an unconstitutional violation of the contract between the state and the board of regents established by the 1812 act. The University of Maryland was a private eleemosynary corporation. The simple act of creation by the state did not make it public. There were no subsequent endowments to make it public. Its purpose, the dissemination of knowledge, no more made it a public corporation than the useful effects of railroads and turnpikes made such institutions public. The 1826 confiscation, Buchanan concluded, was a wholly illegal imposition of state authority.[36]

35. Reverdy Johnson was a Whig but a close friend of John Nelson, a Democrat and one of the most vocal trustees; see Henry Fletcher Powell, *Tercentenary History of Maryland Embodying Biographical Records* . . . (4 vols. Baltimore, 1912), *4*, 889–90.

36. *Regents of the University of Maryland v. Joseph B. Williams*, 9 Gill and Johnson, 365.

Judicial reasoning has sometimes been described as the process of thinking up bad reasons for what is believed on instinct. Whatever Buchanan's instincts, his reasons were indeed very bad. The medical professors had adopted the unwieldy title "Faculty of Physic of the Board of Regents of the University of Maryland." To prove their case they had to demonstrate not only the unconstitutionality of the 1826 act but the validity of their own powers as held by the 1812 act, for the former law effectively abolished the Board of Regents of the College of Medicine authorized by the 1807 act. Buchanan was aware of this objection and argued that both boards of regents continued to exist even after the act of 1812,

> as distinct and independent corporations, in possession of all the rights and franchises conferred upon them by the acts of their incorporation, each having the power to keep and use a public and privy seal; to sue and be sued; to acquire and dispose of property real and personal; to pass by-laws; to grant diplomas; and to perpetuate itself.[37]

But the 1812 act, while not specifically abolishing the Board of Regents of the College of Medicine, stripped it of all its functions. The Regents of the College of Medicine, in other words, were no longer regents over anything, and the intent of the 1807 act was thus plainly defied. If the 1826 act was an unjustifiable interference with a private corporation, so too was the 1812 law.

Buchanan's argument that the private nature of the university rendered it immune from state interference was also questionable. The distinction between public and private corporations was not a part of American law when the university was chartered in 1812. Justice Story used it for the first time in 1815 and again in a concurring opinion in the Dartmouth College case. In the latter case Marshall had relied on his assertion of the contractual nature of a contract, but this was almost as much a novelty as the distinction between public and private corporations. The practice of the Maryland legislature, moreover, had consistently opposed the idea of corporate immunity, and in 1839 a general incorporation law for manufacturing and mining companies expressly reserved to the state the

37. Ibid.

right to amend and repeal at pleasure the charters of such groups. When the Maryland legislature chartered a university in 1812, it had no qualms about reshaping the College of Medicine, and no suspicion that it was irrevocably committing itself to a particular form of government for the university. Either way the subject is approached, then, by the legal standards of 1838 or by those of 1812, Buchanan's resounding affirmation of the inviolable prerogatives of the regents was a shaky piece of reasoning.

Bolstered by the Court of Appeals' ruling, however, the regents petitioned the legislature to relinquish the university's property. Here again legal difficulties were encountered. Most of the valuable property had been acquired by the original board of regents, the Regents of the College of Medicine. If Buchanan was right—and the regents of 1838 certainly thought so—in upholding the validity of the 1812 act by denying that it destroyed the original board, then by what right could the faculty claim the property of the Regents of the College of Medicine? [38] The regents had no ready answer but confidently committed their cause to the Whig majority in the House of Delegates. The vote on the bill to hand over the university to the regents closely followed party lines, with thirty Whigs and seven Democrats supporting the regents and twenty-four Democrats and five Whigs the trustees.[39]

The bill to return the university to the regents was debated repeatedly during the spring of 1839 by the House of Delegates. The final vote was taken two days after the vote on the bill authorizing Thomsonian doctors to sue for fees, but a preliminary vote had already shown that the regents had a clear majority in the House. A comparison of these votes reveals that, as in New York, schisms within a medical college had a damaging effect on efforts to restrict entrance to the profession. A total of 51 delegates took part in the final votes on both issues. Of 31 delegates who supported the regents' position,

38. For a full exposition of this argument, see the House minority report printed in *Report of the Joint Committee on the Memorial of the Regents of the University of Maryland* (Annapolis, 1839).

39. *J. Proc. House of Delegates, Maryland*, Dec. 1838 sess., p. 582. Political affiliations determined from election issues of the *Baltimore American and Commerical Advertiser* (the affiliations of a few regents supporters could not be determined); for the law turning the university back to the regents, see *Laws of Maryland*, Dec. 1838 sess., ch. 334.

16 voted for and 15 against the Thomsonians. But of those favoring the trustees, 20 out of 25 voted for the Thomsonians. The fact that 17 of the 20 voting for both trustees and Thomsonians were Democrats tempts one to argue that their votes were motivated by a typically Jacksonian irreverence toward monopoly grants. Just as the original charter of the University of Maryland could be modified, so too the state was free to revoke the privileges it had once granted to the Medical and Chirurgical Faculty. The Democrats, the argument would conclude, consistently preferred to construe legislative grants narrowly in favor of the state. But explanation purely in terms of political philosophy raises more questions than it answers.

While party lines were sharply drawn on the trustees–regents issue, they were not so drawn, either in Maryland or elsewhere, on the Thomsonian question.[40] If Whigs had a more tender regard for corporate privilege, why was it that nearly half the Whigs voted against the Medical and Chirurgical Faculty? Why did a large number of Democrats oppose the Thomsonians? [41] The best answer is that by 1839 both Whigs and Democrats had united in reaction to grants of exclusive privileges and were vying to outdo each other in devotion to democratic principle. Of the possible voting combinations on the two bills only one noticable correlation could be found. Democrats who supported the trustees voted for the Thomsonians almost to a man. The most plausible explanation is to be found not in terms of political philosophy but in facts of political maneuvering. A large body of Democrats was plainly alienated from the ruling powers of the state's medical profession, from both the medical professors and the Medical and Chirurgical Faculty to which the professors belonged. It is reasonable to suppose that their vote on the Thomsonian bill was largely motivated by a desire to spite the pro-

40. See below, p. 115. Joseph F. Kett, "Regulation of the Medical Profession in America, 1780–1860," Ph.D. thesis (Harvard University, 1964) , p. 43, note 2.

41. Of the twenty delegates supporting both the trustees and the Thomsonians, 17 were Democrats and 3 Whigs; of the 5 who voted against the Thomsonians and for the trustees, 4 were Democrats; of the 15 who supported the regents and opposed the Thomsonians, 11 were Whigs and 4 Democrats; of the 16 supporting both regents and Thomsonians, 12 were Whigs, 2 Democrats, and 2 could not be identified (both coming into the House in by-elections not reported in the newspapers) . The Thomsonians benefited from an alliance between a large number of Whigs and pro-trustee Democrats. Opposing the Thomsonians were, in addition to 13 Whigs, 4 Democrats who voted against the trustees and 6 Democrats who did not vote on the university issue.

fessional men who had shown in the preliminary vote only a few hours earlier that they had the power to wrest the university from Democratic control. The fact that supporters of the regents were about equally divided on the Thomsonian issue is understandable since the Thomsonians were not connected with either political party. The medical professors and through them the Medical and Chirurgical Faculty were, in contrast, very deeply involved in the politics of the state and had to suffer the consequences.

Both the New York and Maryland legislatures acted in 1826 to place medical colleges under outside supervision. In New York this led to the creation of a dissident group of regular physicians who formed a new college and sought repeal of the state's licensing law. In Maryland the professors decided to stay and battle the trustees within the university. But their ultimate success only alienated influential political groups from the profession and inevitably weakened regulatory efforts. The villain in each case was the strength of the proprietary tradition, the assumption that the fortunes of a university were best left to the exclusive direction of its professors. Although rule by the trustees in Maryland had a notably ham-fisted quality, one suspects that any sort of supervision would have been unsatisfactory to a faculty long accustomed to viewing the university as private property.

The controversy, moreover, demoralized the professors of the original faculty. With abundant oportunities elsewhere, the capable professors saw no reason to stay in Baltimore. Pattison had left early in the struggle, and Robley Dunglison and Nathan Ryno Smith departed shortly after 1838. The effect was that Baltimore, which could have supported one strong medical school, was to have a number of weak ones until the emergence of Johns Hopkins.

By the mid-thirties the growing importance of formal medical education was undermining licensing in another respect. Fewer students were disposed to turn to medical societies for licenses. More frequently they simply practiced with only their diplomas as authorization. In Maryland, for example, the licensing role of the Medical and Chirurgical Faculty had been drastically weakened even before 1839. In 1836 medical degrees from the university became valid for practice. Between 1836 and 1840 the Faculty granted only 57 licenses, whereas from 1826 to 1830 it had licensed 134 practitioners.

The struggle between regents and trustees caused many students to leave the state. Those who stayed turned to the medical college, not the medical society, for their qualification.

SOUTH CAROLINA

In 1822 Thomas Cooper of South Carolina College proposed the establishment of a medical college at Columbia, in that state. Cooper had come from England steeped in philosophic radicalism, but he had accommodated many of his views to the prevailing South Carolinian apology for slavery. He had never sacrificed his anti-clericalism, however, and when he was elected president of the college in 1820 over a clergyman, protests were heard from conservative circles. Perhaps owing to his unpopularity in some quarters, perhaps to the existence of a better-organized profession in Charleston, the legislature approved the creation of a medical college but selected Charleston as its site. In 1823 the Medical Society of South Carolina was incorporated as a medical college. Responsibility for the election of professors was placed in the society, but the real impetus came from a number of youthful physicians who had been delivering lectures even before incorporation.

Their leader was Samuel Henry Dickson. Educated at Yale and the University of Pennsylvania, he had also studied in the Charleston office of Philip Gendron Prioleau. Dickson held the chair in medical practice at the new school. United with him on the faculty were James Ramsey, a scion of Scots–Irish parents on the Tennessee frontier, and Edmund Ravenel. Ravenel was a member of the distinguished Huguenot family which had settled in South Carolina after the revocation of the Edict of Nantes. His father was the second Daniel Ravenel of Wantoot, and his mother, Catherine Prioleau, was the daughter of Samuel Prioleau who, when he was a member of the legislature, had spoken on behalf of incorporating the college. Samuel Prioleau's brother was Thomas G. Prioleau, the first professor of obstetrics at the college, and their cousin was Dickson's tutor, Philip G. Prioleau.[42] John E. Holbrook, a noted naturalist, was awarded the professorship of anatomy; the chair in materia

42. *Trans. Huguenot Soc. of South Carolina*, no. 6 (1899), pp. 29–30; *Ravenel Records: A History and Genealogy of the Huguenot Family of Revenel of South Carolina* (Atlanta, 1898), pp. 143–44.

medica went to Henry Frost. A group bound by friendship, youth, ambition, kinship and, as was clear by 1830, success, inevitably stirred resentment in the medical society.

Elder members of the society were diffident about the college's prospects. According to Dickson not even the name of the society would have been given to his followers had they not pledged that "the Society should never be called on to advance a dollar in the prosecution of the affair." [43] But certain younger members such as T. Y. Simons and Jacob de la Motta had hotly contested some of the professorships and were only narrowly defeated. They began to instigate resolutions in the society calling for a detailed report by the faculty of its activities. Then, in 1831, they were presented with the occasion for the "unhappy schism."

Ramsey had repeatedly been accused of public drunkenness and in that year was forced to resign his chair in surgery. There were two candidates to succeed him, John Wagner and Eli Geddings. Geddings was the favorite of the faculty. He was a close friend of Holbrook, the anatomy professor, who had treated him when he was stricken with yellow fever as a student. Despite their preference the society chose Wagner. The manner of the election as well as the result embittered the faculty. The society advertised for candidates, without consulting the professors. Dickson thought this a studied insult, intended to goad the faculty into resigning the chairs, "when they would have been seized upon and divided as spoils of war.[44] A protest was sent to the society, but on motion from Simons it was not considered. At issue were two views of the nature of the college. To the society it was private property managed by the faculty as agents. On the other side, the professors, who had run all the financial risks in establishing the college, demanded a special voice in its affairs, including the right to fill vacancies. They bitterly resented the "inauspicious attention" which had replaced the society's former "friendly inattention" to their affairs.

Rebuffed, the faculty took its case to the legislature and obtained a new charter in 1831. A new board of trustees was created. Of its thirteen members seven were appointed by the society, six by the

43. Samuel H. Dickson, *Statements in Reply to Certain Publications from the Medical Society of South Carolina* (Charleston, 1834), p. 5.
44. Ibid., p. 10.

governor of South Carolina. The trustees nominated by the governor were considered friendly to the faculty. The society, foreseeing a sharp decline in its influence in any event, refused to appoint its quota of trustees and commenced *quo warranto* proceedings against the faculty. Although its position was rejected in the lower courts, the Court of Appeals ruled two to one (with Chancellor Henry W. De Saussure in dissent) that the incorporating act of 1831 violated the Constitutions of South Carolina and the United States.

Both the particulars and legal issues of the case resembled those of *Trustees of Dartmouth College v. Woodward* and *Regents of the University of Maryland v. Joseph B. Williams.* Relying on Marshall's assertion of the contractual nature of a charter, Justice John B. O'Neall concluded that the preamble of the 1823 incorporating act, "a pretty sure guide as to the intention of the Law," made it clear that the contract was between the college (hence the society) and the state. No contract had ever existed between the faculty and the state, and thus the 1831 law, dealing with the faculty of the college as an entity, "is a plain violation of the contract." [45]

The society's victory proved pyrrhic. The faculty was forced to petition for incorporation as a new college, and in 1832 the Medical College of the State of South Carolina was chartered, with the right to confer medical degrees which would be licenses to practice.[46] The already strained relations between the faculty and society were thus severed. The new college had a board of trustees composed of its professors and a number of legislators; Nathaniel Heyward, C. J. Colcock, Henry C. Pinckney, Robert J. Turnbull, Samuel Prioleau, Elias Horry, Jacob Ford, William Drayton, Jasper Adams, H. A. De Saussure, and Mitchel King. The new trustees were not only popular in the state, Turnbull, Colcock, Pinckney, and Heyward being leaders of the nullification party, but many of them were related to the professors. Jacob Ford's brother, Timothy, was a brother-in-law of Edmund Ravenel. Another brother-in-law of Timothy Ford was none other than H. W. De Saussure, the chancellor, a supporter

45. *An Exposition of the Affairs of the Medical College of South Carolina . . .* (Charleston, 1833) , pp. 16–31; *Dartmouth College v. Woodword,* 3 Wheat., 318.

46. The charter is printed in *An Exposition of the Affairs,* pp. 31–33; in 1828 the society decided to dispense with examinations for graduates of the original college. See Minutes, Med. Soc., S.C., Oct. 1, 1828. MSS, library of Medical College of South Carolina.

of the faculty's legal position, and the father of H. A. De Saussure, the trustee. Jacob Ford was on terms of fast friendship with the Prioleau family, and his brother Timothy's second wife was a daughter of Samuel Prioleau. To a large extent the trustees and professors formed an interlocking cousinry, thus ensuring the faculty of continued support in the legislature.[47]

Further, since the trustees were not physicians, they had neither incentive nor interest to scrutinize the activities of the professors. The election of new faculty members was left to the professors, in effect trustees over themselves and proprietors of the college. "The great principle on which we differ from our opponents in the Medical Society," Dickson wrote, "is the advantage or propriety of *Medical Trusteeship*.

> All the world agrees, that too assidious [*sic*] Legislation is in every public case a great evil. In all other matters *"laissez faire"* is as in Commerce the best rule. Any enterprise whatever, must in a great measure be let alone, that is, left to the uncontrolled energies of those immediately engaged and interested in it.[48]

After an undignified struggle for possession of the old college's building, Dickson's faculty was forced to move to new premises on Broad Street. The medical society, still incorporated as a college, chose a new faculty. Three northern physicians, Gunning Bedford and John Rhinelander of New York, and Charles Davis of Pennsylvania, were elected to professorships along with four Carolinians, including T. Y. Simons, the stalwart apologist of the medical society. A thirteen-man board of trustees appointed by the society was given control of the college.

Although driven out of the Medical College of South Carolina, Dickson's faction sought to increase its voice in the affairs of the medical society. In 1834 the society rejected nine candidates for membership because they had been nominated by Dickson's party to enable it to secure a majority. A minority of members, "with very

47. *Ravenel Records*, pp. 143–44; Joseph W. Barnwell, "Diary of Timothy Ford," *S.C. Hist. and Gen. Mag., 12* (July 1912), 132–33; John W. Moore, *Some Family Lines of James Peronneau De Saussure and of His Wife Anna Isabelle De Saussure* (Washington, 1958), p. 3.
48. Dickson, *Statements in Reply*, p. 8.

few exceptions, either professors and lecturers, or relatives of professors in a Rival Medical Institution," protested the rejection.[49]
But Dickson was outmaneuvered. Failing a majority, his followers
were barred from all offices of the society in May 1835. This scrim-
maging, however, was weakening both factions instead of strengthen-
ing either.

Of the two medical schools, one participant in the controversy
noted that only one could prosper, but both might perish. Under its
new administration the Medical College of South Carolina was a
failure. "Our opponents," Simons conceded, "had been for years
organized under all the auspices and influence of this Society. They
had their friends and former pupils, as well as their graduates, settled throughout different sections of the Country." To this advantage
the "political influence" of Dickson's faculty was added, and Simons
drew the society's attention to the fact that:

> *Your* College is the "Medical College of South Carolina,"
> the rival College is the "Medical College of the State of
> South Carolina," and the word "State" superadded together
> with the circumstances that some of our Professors were
> from the North, has led to the inference . . . that the for-
> mer was the College of the *State*, while the other must
> necessarily, in public opinion, naturally possess political
> feelings opposed to this State.[50]

But Simons was not simply the victim of prejudice generated by
the Nullification Crisis. His rivals had established an infirmary with
much lower rates than those sanctioned by a fee table of 1820 which
governed the society. Unable to attract enough students, the faculty

49. John Bellinger, *A History of "the Stamp Act" of the Medical Society of South-
Carolina* (Charleston, 1835), p. 5; *Report of a Committee appointed to reply to the
Protest of a minority of the Members of the Medical Society of South-Carolina*
(Charleston, 1835), pp. 2–6. The minority report was signed by Philip G. Prioleau,
Christopher C. Pritchard, William Michel, Alexander Baron, A. G. Howard, William
T. Wragg, James P. Jervey, Thomas M. Logan, James Moultrie and James Moultrie,
Jr., S. H. Dickson, T. G. Prioleau, J. G. W. Wurdemann, and John Bellinger. The
Moultries were descendants of Dr. John Moultrie, a brother of Major General William
Moultrie, the Revolutionary hero. They were related to the Ravenels, and hence to
the Prioleaus, De Saussures, and Fords, by the marriage of Daniel Ravenel of Wantoot
to General Moultrie's sister-in-law; see *S.C. Hist. and Gen. Mag., 5* (Oct. 1904), 247–48.
50. Minutes, Med. Soc., S.C., March 2, 1835.

of the Medical College of South Carolina resigned at the end of 1837. The medical society barely survived the "unhappy schism." It maintained a trancelike existence in ensuing years, with rarely more than five or six physicians attending its meetings.

By 1838 there were two effective licensing agencies in South Carolina, the medical society and the Medical College of the State of South Carolina. The legislature was principally occupied with arbitrating disputes between the agencies and had little time to supervise the standards of either. Regulation of medical practice thus became an entirely professional responsibility, but the profession, demoralized by internal feuds, was incapable of discharging its task.

AMERICA AND CANADA

The return from Scotland after 1760 of a number of enthusiastic and qualified medical scientists created a group ready to petition legislatures to incorporate medical societies and faculties. Each charter, however, only expanded the room at the top, whetting appetites for more charters. Several factors aggravated the original weakness of corporate restraints arising from the absence of ancient institutions. Since both medical societies and medical schools were licensing agencies, any wrangling between them undermined the attempt to regulate practice. Unfortunately, there was almost constant wrangling, due partly to conflicts of personalities, partly to rivalry in the field of licensing, and partly to the tendency to use the corporate status of medical societies as a catapult to professorships.

The gradual ascendency of medical schools over medical societies created even more serious problems. In Britain the regulatory societies had been firmly rooted in the history of guild organization, but in America medical schools antedated the societies in some places and were established coincidentally in others. In the nineteenth century the societies dwindled in importance, yielding, albeit reluctantly, many of their functions to medical schools. American medical schools, however, were ill prepared for such a role. Medical schools generally arose out of private instruction classes, and any relation they had to existing academic institutions was at best a marriage of convenience. Proprietary medical schools were not unknown in England but, unable to grant degrees, they were doomed to a minor niche in British medical education. In America they came to form the basis of medical instruction. Operating without outside restraint, their activities quickly took on molecular characteristics, bouncing about at random, smacking into each other, forming chance alliances, and breaking into still smaller particles.

An instructive comparison can be drawn between the shaky beginnings of the American medical profession and the medical history of Upper Canada. Upper Canada (Canada West after 1841) confronted many of the same problems that plagued the American profession. Canadian physicians were constantly pleading for stricter enforcement of the licensing laws.[51] Professional rivalries were sharp. On a number of occasions dissidents withdrew from existing medical schools to start rivals. The proprietary school made its appearance. But Canada never experienced anything like the institutional disorganization that marked the American profession, even though the physical problems—a scattered population and difficulties in communication—were at least as severe as in the United States.

Despite complaints about nonenforcement and despite an influx of botanic practitioners from the United States after 1830, licensing laws remained in force throughout the century. A licensing board established in 1818 at York (now Toronto) conducted rigorous examinations; between 1830 and 1837 nearly a third of the candidates were rejected.[52] The examinations were so rigorous in fact that a number of physicans, witnessing with dismay the high casualty rate among their students, began in 1836 to agitate for a change in the membership of the board. Canada was then on the brink of a rebellion. Dissatisfaction with the generally oligarchic character of the nation threatened violence. But the principle of regulation of the profession survived the political upheavals of 1837. The licensing board added a few members but continued to function as before.

The causes of Canada's success in licensing were partly psychological and partly institutional. Canadian nationalism then as now contained a strong dosage of anti-Americanism. There were wide-

51. William Canniff, *The Medical Profession in Upper Canada, 1783–1850. An Historical Narrative, with Original Documents relating to the Profession, including Some Brief Biographies* (Toronto, 1894).

52. Ibid., p. 103; there is a documentary review of Canadian licensing legislation in John Joseph Heagerty, *Four Centuries of Medical History in Canada* (2 vols. Toronto, 1928), *1*, 316–27. After 1841 a license in Canada West was valid in Canada East and vice versa; see ibid., p. 325. Licenses were granted in all or one of the branches.

spread fears that, in the absence of licensing, battalions of American quacks armed as much with republicanism as with charlatanism would invade Canada. But, perhaps even more important, there were no institutions around which opposition to the medical licensng board could rally. There were no incorporated medical societies and, before 1840, no incorporated medical schools in Upper Canada. Dissatisfaction with the York licensing board was confined to public protests, never an especially effective way of getting things accomplished in early nineteenth-century Canada.[53]

After 1840 a number of medical schools came into existence in Upper Canada.[54] Since the York licensing board did not examine medical graduates, a proliferation of medical schools could have undermined the regulatory system. But a variety of factors checked increase in numbers. First of all, though the earliest medical schools were proprietary they could not grant degrees until they established a university connection. The case of the Toronto School of Medicine —the so-called Rolph's school—offers a good illustration of the problems of the Canadian proprietary school. John Rolph, one of the more flamboyant figures in early Canadian medical history, began to give lectures at St. Thomas in 1824. Later he moved to York but, after siding with Mackenzie in the disturbances of 1837, he had to flee to the United States. After proclamation of an amnesty he returned to York and continued to teach. But without a university affiliation his school could not grant degrees. In this respect the Canadian proprietary school was identical with its British counter-

53. As Samuel E. Morison has noted in his *Oxford History of the American People* (New York, 1965), while Canada paralleled America's development in some ways, in others it was "dissimilar as if on a separate continent"; see also Donald Creighton, *Dominion of the North: A History of Canada* (Boston, 1944), pp. 236–37.

54. Instruction began at King's College in 1844 and stopped in 1851. Victoria, Queen's, and Trinity universities also had medical departments. The last university was founded by Bishop Strachan, the Anglican leader, after King's became part of the secular University of Toronto in 1849. See F. Arnold Clarkson, "The Medical Faculty of the University of Toronto: History of Canadian Medical Schools—IV," *Hist. Bull.: Calgary Associate Clinic, 13* (Aug. 1948), 21–30; W. T. Connell, "The Medical Faculty of Queen's University: History of Canadian Medical Schools—V," ibid., *13* (Nov. 1948), 45–50; D. D. Calvin, *Queen's University of Kingston, 1841–1941* (Kingston, 1941), pp. 191–97. Medical education had an earlier start in Lower Canada; the Montreal Medical Institute began operations in 1823–24 and in 1829 it became the medical department of McGill University, though at that time virtually no other teaching was going on at McGill.

part. Rolph had his school made the medical department of Victoria University at Cobourg and later of the University of Toronto. In practice his students, even after his affiliation with universities, spent their final year at McGill or at one of the better American schools like Jefferson in Philadelphia.[55]

The connection between a proprietary school and a university was often a tenuous one, but any kind of affiliation served the purpose of automatically limiting the number of schools to the number of universities. In the United States, where the multiplication of medical schools in the early nineteenth century paralleled a general proliferation of colleges and universities, this would not have been an important factor. But in Upper Canada government policy kept a ceiling on the number of universities. Each denomination could boast of one major school: Victoria for the Methodists, Queen's for the Presbyterians, and King's College (later part of the secular University of Toronto) for the Angelicans. In the United States every denomination and nearly every offshoot of every denomination had a number of colleges or universities by 1850. The restriction on the number of medical schools in Upper Canada made it possible to keep some kind of national supervision over the quality of medical education and made the task of the licensing board at York more manageable.

In the United States medical schools were constantly at odds with the licensing agencies, the medical societies. Members of the latter often took advantage of the incorporated and hence semiofficial status

55. Rolph's school had a complex history. In 1856 his colleagues ejected Rolph. A legal battle over use of the name "Toronto School of Medicine" ensued. Rolph lost, and, while he continued to lecture in a separate building, he had to call his establishment simply "Rolph's School." This school became part of Victoria University while the Toronto School of Medicine later became the medical department of the University of Toronto; see Malcolm H. V. Cameron, "Medical Education in Toronto," *Hist. Bull.: Calgary Associate Clinic*, *17* (Feb. 1953), 71–74; G. D. Stanley, "Physicians in Canadian History—VII: Dr. John Rolph," ibid., *9* (May 1944), 1–13. The history of the medical faculty of Queen's University was similar in some respects to that of Rolph's school. In 1854 dissenting students at the Anglican Trinity University asked the trustees of Queen's (Presbyterian) to establish a medical faculty. For the next ten years the medical department of Queen's feuded constantly with the trustees. Finally, in 1866, the medical department incorporated itself as the Royal College of Physicians and Surgeons of Kingston. But the Royal College still had to maintain a tenuous relation with Queen's since the former's degrees were granted in the name of Queen's University. See Calvin, *Queen's University of Kingston, 1841–1941*, pp. 196–97.

of their societies to agitate for control of existing medical schools, usually with an eye to obtaining professorships for themselves. Upper Canada avoided the American technique of incorporating county or district societies to regulate the profession and hence removed a source of friction between professors and practitioners. One attempt was made to incorporate the York licensing board, but it proved abortive. In 1839 the board was chartered as the College of Physicians and Surgeons of Upper Canada. The absence of formal medical instruction in York had long chagrined members of the board, and they hoped that the college would be a stepping-stone to professorships for themselves. But the government disallowed the charter in 1840 as conferring excessive power on the board and thus eliminated another potential source of institutional disorganization.[56]

While the example of Upper Canada indicates that New World conditions did not have to have a disintegrating effect on professional organization, certain qualifications should be noted before one exaggerates the degree of disorganization within the American profession. The proprietary medical school, bad as it was, was not a wholly negative influence. From a medical standpoint its principal defects were low standards and the complete absence of inducements to raise standards. But had medical schools been integral parts of universities it is still doubtful that requirements would have been upgraded. A medical degree was not a necessity for practice, and schools were not the only places where medicine could be learned. Medical colleges were always in danger of pricing themselves out of the market. If standards went up, enrollment would go down, but the number of people calling themselves doctors would not have decreased. The only losers would have been the professors.

A related defect was that as long as schools were under proprietary control there could be no way of ensuring that adequate scientific facilities would be provided. But this is an unrealistic objection in view of the state of medical science in the 1830s. Most professors simply would not have known what to do with a well-financed

56. Canniff, *The Medical Profession*, pp. 95–102, 112, 121; the head of the board, Christopher Widmer, was the moving spirit behind the incorporation. He was also a leader of the Medico-Chirurgical Society of Upper Canada, founded in 1833. This was the only medical society in Ontario. It was not incorporated and had few members. For a discussion of this and later Canadian medical societies, see Heagerty, *Four Centuries of Medical History, 1*, 285ff.

laboratory, and it is highly unlikely in any event that parent universities would have set up such laboratories. When the work of Hopkins scientists in the late nineteenth century won respect for the German laboratory tradition, the prevalence of proprietary schools proved a hindrance to incorporating that tradition into medical science. But the world of Daniel Coit Gilman, William S. Halsted, and William H. Welch was not the world of David Hosack, John B. Davidge, and Samuel H. Dickson.

The rapid spread of medical schools wrought havoc with medical societies. The proprietary tradition in state after state wrecked licensing efforts. But here the most important qualification must be made. By the mid-thirties the futility of prosecuting unlicensed practitioners was obvious. Licensing was not serving the purpose it had begun to acquire after 1760—the suppression of incompetent practice. Its only real effect was the separation of semiqualified from wholly unqualified practitioners. This had been the original purpose of a license. Prior to 1760 a license had been no more than a testimonial of superior qualification. But by 1830 medical degrees had taken over to a great extent the function of identifying qualified physicians, and were performing the function at least as well as licenses had ever done. The decline of the licensing role of medical societies was thus offset in large measure. Had the degree been difficult to obtain, no more than a fraction of the actual practitioners would have taken any form of qualification. The medical profession would have been confined to the fringe of practice. The facility with which degrees could be obtained ensured that a fairly high percentage of practitioners was brought into the organized medical fraternity. While the state of their preparation left much to be desired, this was still a vast improvement over conditions before 1760 when the establishment of an identifiable profession outside of a few large cities had been extremely difficult.

THREE

The Perils of Control

On water see him swim
And not the surface shake
All smooth and light and trim—
The treacherous DOCTOR DRAKE!

Cincinnati broadside, 1838

The proprietary tradition led to multiplication of medical schools, with advantages and disadvantages. On one level proliferation created chaos, antagonism between medical schools and medical societies, and undermining of licensing efforts. On another level it provided a way of identifying trained practitioners to the public in a nation where traditional devices for such identification—guilds and medical societies—either did not exist or had little influence.

The pattern in New York, Maryland, and South Carolina was for a medical society to start a medical school. Professors at the school soon tired of the meddling of the parent body and severed connections. One of two developments ensued. Either the parent body then turned to the state and convinced government officials of the wisdom of assuming direction of the school, or dissident members of the faculty, unable to force their wishes on their fellow professors, decided also to seek state intervention. Though state intervention was a convenient method of appeasing dissidents, it infuriated the original professors who usually abandoned the school to start a rival.

A question, hitherto latent but now deserving of separate study, is whether state intervention in the formation of medical schools was desirable. The problem can best be approached by analyzing the medical history of two states where institutional control was effective, Massachusetts and Ohio. Each state discouraged the multiplication of medical schools that plagued other sections of the country in the 1830s. A delicate alliance of the legislature, Harvard, and the state medical society in Massachusetts, and government policy in Ohio, checked the emergence of serious rivals to the state's original medical college. The results were generally happy in Massachusetts, but in Ohio medical scientists sought to use the Jacksonian and Whig parties to their own advantage with disastrous results.

MASSACHUSETTS

In 1782, a year after the incorporation of the Massachusetts Medical Society, a medical school was established at Harvard. John Warren, a young anatomy lecturer, was chiefly responsible for its inception and early success. Graduated from Harvard College in 1771, Warren began to study medicine under his older brother Joseph, who was fatally wounded at Bunker Hill. The younger Warren was also eager to join the infantry, but his mother and friends persuaded him to enter the medical department of the army. In 1776, at the age of twenty-two, he was appointed by General Washington senior surgeon to the military hospital at Cambridge. In May of that year he accompanied the army to Long Island and later shared its trials in the New Jersey and Pennsylvania campaigns. Returning to Boston in July 1777, Warren married Abigail Collins, the daughter of the governor of Rhode Island, and resumed direction of the military hospital.

The fluctuation of continental money was causing distress to physicians. To discuss their difficulties a number formed a club—the Boston Medical Society—which met at the Green Dragon tavern. After one of their gatherings Isaac Rand observed to Ephraim Eliot that "Warren is an artful man, and will soon get to windward of us all". . .

> He has made a proposition to the club, that as there are nearly a dozen pupils studying in town, there should be an incipient medical school instituted here for their benefit; and has nominated Danforth to read the theory and practice of physic, and some suitable person on anatomy and surgery. *He* was immediately put up for the latter branches; and, after a little maiden coyness, agreed to commence a course, as he has had many operations and surgical cases in the Continental Hospital, of which he is the sole director

in every respect; . . . But he will not stop there; he well knows that moneys have been left to the college for such an establishment as he is appointed to, and he is looking at the professorship. *Mark what I say, Eliot: you will probably live to see it verified.*[1]

Warren was indeed aware of the bequest of Ezekiel Hersey of Hingham for the establishment of a resident professorship of anatomy and surgery at Harvard. Improvements on the legacy by Hersey's widow and brothers led the corporation to ponder seriously the creation of a medical school, and Warren's success as a free-lance lecturer recommended him strongly for the anatomy chair. Additional funds were raised for professorships in chemistry and medicine. To fill the former, the corporation selected Aaron Dexter, a graduate of Harvard and student of Boston's leading chemist, Samuel Danforth. The chair of medicine was awarded to Benjamin Waterhouse, a young Quaker physician and colleague of the celebrated London physician John Lettsom.

The Massachusetts Medical Society greeted the new medical school with some hostility. The society's incorporating act seemed to grant it an exclusive right to license, but Harvard viewed the acknowledged privileges of universities as sufficient authority to render its medical degrees licenses. Repeated conferences between the two bodies terminated in agreement. A Harvard diploma or letters testimonial from the society were alike considered as entitling a physician to practice and to use the society's excellent library.[2]

However renowned Harvard College was, its medical school was still an infant and was not to mature without a difficult adolescence. The school's early difficulties were largely due to a feud between Waterhouse and his fellow professors. The points at issue were legion. Although his chair was in medicine, Waterhouse began in 1788

1. "Dr. Ephraim Eliot's Account of the Physicians of Boston," *Proc., Mass. Hist. Soc.,* 7 (1863) , pp. 177ff.
2. Walter L. Burrage, *A History of the Massachusetts Medical Society* (privately printed, 1923) , p. 305. Perhaps the earliest occasion of friction between the medical society and the new medical school arose in 1784 when a number of Boston doctors protested Harvard's attempt to persuade the Commonweatlh to establish an infirmary for clinical study near the university. See Thomas F. Harrington, *The Harvard Medical School: A History, Narrative, and Documentary, 1782–1905,* ed. James Mumford (3 vols. New York, 1905) , *1*, 275.

to give lectures on natural history. His correspondence with scientists abroad led to the acquisition of various specimens and the formation of a mineral and zoological cabinet which he supervised for a nominal fee. Waterhouse kept the cabinet and delivered lectures in the Philosophy Chamber, the room adjoining the library in Harvard Hall. Competition for space arose between Waterhouse and Samuel Webber, the Hollis Professor of Mathematics, who used the chamber also and found the decor of rocks and stuffed birds distracting.[3] Since the medical professors had been assigned Holden Chapel for their lectures, Waterhouse was asked to relinquish the Philosophy Chamber. No professor in the college had adequate space, but Waterhouse took his explusion as a personal slight and complained that he had been reduced to the expedient of lecturing in the room of an undergraduate.

Further insult and injury were soon added. Friends of the college subscribed to the foundation of a professorship of natural history. Waterhouse felt that he would be given the chair as a reward for his faithful service to the mineral cabinet. But it was awarded to another, and in 1807 a corporation committee charged Waterhouse with neglect of the cabinet and recommended his dismissal from its care.[4]

Behind these disagreements was the growing antagonism between Waterhouse and John Warren. Warren's son, John Collins Warren, had taken his medical degree from Harvard in 1797 and was soon appointed adjunct professor of anatomy. Waterhouse had similar ambitions for his own son, a lad of "respectable talents and uncommon industry," and confided this favorite idea to John Warren. The latter's reaction to this species of emulation is not recorded but, in light of Waterhouse's later accusations, it must have been unenthusiastic.

Warren was developing a favorite idea of his own, the removal

3. William Coolidge Lane, Dr. Benjamin Waterhouse and Harvard University (reprinted from Proc., Cambridge Hist. Soc., 4, Jan. 1909), 9. Waterhouse described Webber as a "sort of negative character; a man without friends or enemies; a man as ignorant of the world as if he had never been born into it; a mere mathematician; to which branch of science he is a bigot; a man who thinks that all the rest of the world are busy about trifles, mathematicians excepted;" quoted in ibid., p. 16. When Webber was made President of Harvard College, Waterhouse was naturally chagrined.

4. Papers relating to the Waterhouse Controversy, 1812, p. 26. MSS, Harvard College Library.

of the medical school to Boston. Conflicting versions of Waterhouse's attitude were given. Warren alleged that Waterhouse opposed removal and took steps to exclude the latter from the Boston Almshouse, where lectures were to be given. Waterhouse claimed that he only wanted adequate time "to consider the matter in all its relations" and objected to the haughtiness of his colleagues in memorializing the corporation for removal without consulting him.

The truth was that Waterhouse was unwilling to follow John Warren anywhere, least of all to Boston. Removal would only bring him closer to his *bête noire* of long duration, the Massachusetts Medical Society. In 1799 Waterhouse had received from his friend Dr. Lettsom a copy of Edward Jenner's *Inquiry into the Causes and Effects of the Variolae Vaccinae*. Soon afterward he imported cowpox virus and carried out several successful vaccinations. He attempted at first to monopolize the vaccine, for reasons not entirely selfish. A few disastrous vaccinations by incompetent practitioners would have seriously retarded the introduction of Jenner's technique. On the other hand, Waterhouse was a promoter, not the originator, of the vaccine. Members of the Massachusetts Medical Society, of which Warren was vice-president, saw no reason to honor his monopoly and successfully broke it. When Waterhouse later sought to establish a vaccine institute for gratuitous vaccination of the poor, the society again checked his efforts.[5]

Waterhouse blamed his real and fancied grievances on John Warren. Malice was never one of Warren's traits. Contemporaries thought him the most benign of men. His dislike of Waterhouse transcended any specific issue and was shared by all his colleagues. Waterhouse had the zeal and arrogance of the innovator and, in addition, a sensitivity to criticism that bordered on paranoia. "Ever since I had the hardihood to vaccinate in the town of Boston without permission or license from those who assumed the direction and control of our little medical world," Waterhouse wrote, "these Boston Doctors have considered me as *a football* to kick about for their amusement." [6] His writings abound with references to his "accusers." Even the simplest questions elicited crusty retorts from him. Did Waterhouse write an attack on Warren in a Boston newspaper, a trustee asked?

5. John B. Blake, *Benjamin Waterhouse and the Introduction of Vaccination: A Reappraisal* (Philadelphia, 1957), chs. 1–5.
6. Papers relating to the Waterhouse Controversy, p. 37.

"I hesitated," Waterhouse replied, "as I wished to know *on what principle* this part of the enquiry was to proceed:

> I said that I was accused and my accusers must prove the charge; and I said that I should deny the whole on the principle of pleading *"not guilty"* in court; the meaning of which is "prove it." Mr. Lovel observed, and I thought justly, that there was a considerable difference between a court of law, and such a *court of honor* as that. All my arguing was merely to know, and to establish the *principle* on which to proceed; for I had fully determined on my principle before I waited on the Corporation. Mr. Lovel and I argued exactly as to the propriety of asking a man, in common cases, *if he wrote such and such pieces in the newspapers.*[7]

Reluctant to leave Cambridge, Waterhouse was equally unwilling to lose his professorship. The obvious solution was a new medical school. For some time before 1811 Waterhouse had been corresponding with a group interested in establishing a Massachusetts College of Physicians. The college could be a medical society to rival the Massachusetts Medical Society, or a medical school to rival Harvard, or both. As usual, confusion arose as to Waterhouse's intentions. He told Warren that his sole concern was for a new medical society, but Warren alleged that Waterhouse really desired a new school. Since Waterhouse was estranged from all parties, either interpretation is plausible. A series of events in 1811 brought alignments into the open.

A body of physicians led by Samuel Danforth, and including John Jeffries, William Aspinwall, Nathaniel Ames, and Thomas Williams, petitioned for incorporation of the new college, ostensibly because "two literary and scientific bodies produce more than double the advantage of one." [8] Their goal was probably a new medical school; Danforth had never forgiven himself for letting his student, Aaron Dexter, walk off with the chemistry professorship at Harvard. But

7. Benjamin Waterhouse, "Apology to the Corporation for Novum Organum," March 3, 1812. MS, Harvard College Library. Waterhouse had published a number of attacks on Warren in the *New England Palladium;* see issues for April 23, 26, and May 3, 1811.

8. The petition is printed in Burrage, *A History of the Massachusetts Medical Society,* pp. 77–78.

since it was still not absolutely certain that the petitioners desired a new school and not a new society, the Massachusetts Medical Society united with Harvard in violently protesting their petition. The immediate effect of this was to cause the original petitioners to withdraw their names, but their places were quickly taken by five new petitioners led by the indefatigable Waterhouse, who had resigned his Harvard chair shortly after removal of the medical school to Boston in 1811.

Waterhouse, a maverick down to his Jeffersonian political views, advertised the college as a means of offsetting Federalist influence in existing scientific institutions. John C. Warren took up the challenge in *A Letter Addressed to a Republican Member of the House of Representatives of the State of Massachusetts*. Among the original petitioners, Danforth and Jefferies had been staunch loyalists in 1776; Nathaniel Ames was the brother of the arch-Federalist Fisher Ames. Together they hardly formed the components of a rampaging Jeffersonian faction. After reviewing the chaos attendant on the incorporation of the College of Physicians and Surgeons as a rival to Columbia, Warren concluded that it was "vain to expect political influence from scientific societies." [9]

His efforts drew a reply from the Republican side, allegedly written by Joseph Story but probably the work of one of the younger physicians in Waterhouse's faction, if not Waterhouse himself. Warren had claimed that the college threatened both the Massachusetts Medical Society and Harvard. *An Answer* asserted, however, that it endangered only Harvard, "one of the most nefarious and powerful engines in erecting a detestable aristocracy, and destroying the vital principles of republicanism," and that Warren's only concern was "to protect the exclusive privileges and honours, you and your family enjoy under the patronage of the University at Cambridge," a concern manifested "by the anile whinings that have escaped you whenever you have mentioned the Medical School of Harvard University." The argument of Warren's *Letter* "is precisely the same used by your party in opposition to the State Bank and religious bill, . . . the

9. John Warren [?] (Boston, 1812), p. 11. On the authorship of this pamphlet see chapter 2, note 8. Warren noted that one of the reasons for chartering the College of Physicians and Surgeons was to offset Federalist influence at Columbia, but he emphasized that any political gains were quickly nullified by professional feuding which cut across party lines.

whole of your communication is in the true spirit of that monopoly you have so long and so tyranically exercised." [10] Massachusetts was a Federalist state, however, and Waterhouse had arrayed himself against the Massachusetts Medical Society and Harvard. Despite *An Answer* his petition was rejected.

The pattern elsewhere was for a disgruntled physician to ally himself with an incorporated medical society and then petition for a new school. But Waterhouse's cantankerousness had separated him from all parties; his proposed College of Physicians threatened everyone. His few allies were significant for their insignificance. Thus his feud with Warren began and ended as a conflict of personalities.

Among those opposing the petition had been Henry Halsey Childs, a Pittsfield physician. After the collapse of Waterhouse's scheme, Childs served in the legislature where he agitated for incorporation of a medical college in Berkshire. His efforts were partly successful in 1823 when the Berkshire Medical Institution was chartered. Situated in Pittsfield, it was practically a department of nearby Williams College, under whose name its degrees were conferred. Taking comfort from Berkshire's remoteness, Harvard and the Massachusetts Medical Society nevertheless viewed the school with suspicion. They successfully maintained before the courts that, as the Berkshire school did not have an independent board of visitors, its graduates should not be allowed to practice on the sole authorization of their diplomas. James Jackson, for example, feared that in the absence of such a board the school would go the way of the "Scotch universities," a reference to Aberdeen and St. Andrews Universities, which engaged in the virtual sale of medical degrees throughout the eighteenth century. These objections were met in 1837 by revision of the school's charter with provision for a board of visitors. Berkshire graduates thereafter had all the privileges of Harvard graduates, but the school had little reputation and could not lure the better students away from Boston. Eastern physicians viewed it more as an occasionally useful ally than as a rival.

Harvard and the medical society formed a permanent lobby against the chartering of schools closer to Boston. Many of the distinguished local physicians gave private lectures, often at night or during vacations, to Harvard medical students. The function of these

10. Joseph Story [?], *An Answer to a Letter* . . . (Boston, 1812), pp. 3–4, 15.

private schools was similar to that of the famous Great Windmill Street School in London, to supplement rather than to compete with incorporated medical schools. When the faculty of one such institution, the Boylston Medical School, petitioned for incorporation, it met with opposition from James Jackson, Oliver Wendell Holmes, and Jacob Bigelow of Harvard, who called attention to the languishing state of most New England medical schools because of the small number of their students. The overcrowded state of the profession, "there being probably five times as many physicians as the public requires in the Commonwealth," was not conducive to further incorporations.[11] Influenced by these considerations the legislature rejected the petition and a similar request from a group intending to establish a school in Lowell.

The death of Samuel Thomson in 1843 removed the last obstacle to the establishment of botanic medical colleges in New England. Convinced that medical principles were within the grasp of every man, Thomson resolutely opposed special training for physicians. His followers, however, were more diffident of self-medication and insisted on formal education. In 1846 a botanic school was established in Worcester. But opposition from Harvard, the Berkshire Medical Institution, and the Massachusetts Medical Society thwarted its attempts to obtain a charter until 1852. By the time the New England Botanico-Medical College was incorporated the Thomsonian movement was in decline. Attendance fell off after 1854 and lectures were suspended in 1859.

In addition to avoiding conflict between rival medical schools, the Commonwealth also averted the excess of local autonomy that characterized New York's medical societies. The district societies authorized by the 1803 law were not separate corporations but branches of a single governing corporation. Their privileges were few: the making of bylaws (consistent with those of the parent society), the collection of dues (the bulk of which had to be transferred to the society), and the election of their own officers (except for censors, appointed by the society). By 1820 dissatisfaction with

11. "Remonstrance to the Legislature of the Faculty of the Massachusetts Medical College, against the Petition of the Boylston Medical School for Power to confer Medical Degrees," *Boston Med. Surg. J.,* 50 (April 26, 1854), 260. The Massachusetts Medical College was the name often used for the medical school of Harvard.

these arrangements was growing. In 1831 it assumed the form of concrete proposals for change.

A district society had been incorporated in Berkshire in 1820, but Childs, the articulate spokesman for western interests, claimed that it was in a state of declension because of the few privileges the members received, and the unreasonable expense connected with it. To remedy this he called for a complete reorganization. The Massachusetts Medical Society, in his view, should become a federation of powerful district societies. His immediate goal was a separate charter for the Berkshire District Society. In opposition, the Massachusetts Medical Society foresaw the failure of "all attempts to preserve uniformity," if a number of independent boards of censors was established. Childs' request was denied, but the society moved to appease its western faction in other ways. Childs had a legitimate grievance over the payment of dues. Prior to 1832 the district treasurers could keep only 5 per cent. The remainder was deposited in Boston for upkeep of the society's library and building. There were no district libraries, but some books from the central library were loaned to the district societies. In 1832 the latter were allowed to keep one third of the dues for purchase of books. But not until 1848 were they given a direct voice in managing the parent society's affairs. Thereafter councillors were elected by fellows in the several districts, and provision was made for rotating the annual convention among the major cities of the Commonwealth.[12]

The society's affairs, however, continued under eastern dominance. Although vice-presidents were occasionally drawn from the west, no western fellow was elected president of the society until 1870. Berkshire was given more than a sop but less than parity. Further, the principle of centralization, having survived the crisis of 1831, was never again sharply challenged. When the society's position was shaken just before the Civil War, the cause was its failure to overcome homoeopathy, not internal discord.

Ohio

Alongside the early medical history of Ohio the stories of the preceding states seem like tales from a McGuffey reader. For sheer vituperation nothing could quite match Ohio medical broils. Not

12. Burrage, *A History of the Massachusetts Medical Society*, p. 84.

only did Ohio physicians enter the political arena with greater zeal than their counterparts elsewhere but, in addition, Ohio professional rivalries had a more personal, vindictive tone. In 1820 John Moorhead fired a question at Daniel Drake in a Cincinnati newspaper: "But you, Sir—what are you?" Moorhead had a ready answer:

> The common breaker of the medical peace—the common violator of the medical law—the common disturber of medical harmony—the common fomenter of medical broils —the common invader of medical rights—the common pest of medical society.[13]

Moorhead's performance was not out of character for him, for his cohorts, or in fact for Drake. By Ohio professional standards it was almost good form; the rough and ready tone of Ohio life pervaded the medical profession as much as it imbued elections or Fourth of July orations. The frequency of public canings and fistfights within the "medical fraternity" leaves the historian with no problem in distinguishing professional alignments in Ohio.

The protagonist of Ohio medical history in the antebellum period was Daniel Drake. Born in New Jersey and raised in Kentucky, Drake came to Cincinnati in 1800 as an apprentice to a local doctor. He returned to the East in 1805 to study under Rush, Philip Syng Physick, and Casper Wistar at the medical department of the University of Pennsylvania. Following the common practice Drake did not stay long enough to take a degree from Pennsylvania but, after practicing briefly at Mays Lick, Kentucky, he went back to Cincinnati in 1807. His life in Cincinnati was often a vexatious one, but his decision to practice there was wise. Its location on the Ohio River and its position as portal to the rich hinterlands between the Ohio and Miami rivers was establishing Cincinnati as mistress of the Ohio Valley. In his lifetime Drake saw his adopted city wrest first economic and then cultural leadership from Lexington, hitherto the acknowledged Athens of the West. Further, the absence of established lines of leadership in the city allowed a newcomer like Drake scope for his exceptional scientific talents and unrestrained ambition.[14]

13. *Liberty Hall and Cincinnati Gazette,* Feb. 4, 1820.
14. Emmet F. Horine, *Daniel Drake (1785–1852): Pioneer Physician of the Midwest*

From 1807 until 1815 Drake built a substantial private practice and devoted himself to civic improvements, writing two sketches to publicize the city, starting a debating society and library, and encouraging the foundation of the Western Museum Society which he endowed with his own "extensive collections of minerals, bones of the mammoths, and antiquities of the West." On two occasions Drake left the city, in 1816 to secure his medical degree at Pennsylvania and in 1817 when he accepted a professorship at Transylvania University in Lexington. Disgusted with internal feuding in the Transylvania medical faculty, however, Drake resigned his chair in 1818 and returned to Cincinnati.

Drake first conceived of starting a medical school in Cincinnati in 1817, and by spring 1818 he had commenced private lectures with the aid of Coleman Rogers, who practiced medicine in partnership with Drake, and the Rev. Elijah Slack, a manager of the Western Museum Society and president of the Lancasterian Seminary.[15] Neither Rogers nor Slack contributed much to the school. Drake did nearly all the teaching, covering medical practice, botany, materia medica, and physiology. The only question is why he associated at all with Rogers and Slack. He probably hoped that a school staffed by a faculty of three would have a better chance of securing a charter than a one-man operation.

Without great difficulty Drake obtained a charter in 1819. The Medical College of Ohio was a proprietary venture in every sense of the word. There was not even a nominal university connection as in Maryland. The incorporation act provided that the Ohio Medical Convention designate two visitors to the college, but given the moribund nature of the Medical Convention, little effective supervision could be expected from that quarter. Shortly after incorporation of the Medical College the legislature also chartered Cincinnati College to replace the Lancasterian Seminary, with the Rev. Mr. Slack as president and a list of local notables, including Drake, as trustees. To have made Drake's medical school a department of the new college would have posed no problem since the charter of Cin-

(Philadelphia, 1961), ch. 3; Daniel Aaron, "Cincinnati, 1818–1838: A Study of Attitudes in the Urban West," Ph.D. thesis (Harvard University, 1942), pp. 10–41.

15. So called because it was modeled on the monitorial principles of the English educational reformer, Joseph Lancaster.

cinnati College entitled it to confer "all or any of the degrees that are usually conferred in any college or university within the United States." That Drake could have induced the legislature to keep separate a college and a medical school chartered in the same city is an emblem of his personal magnetism and impatience with restraint.

No medical school in pre-Civil War America had a more hectic existence than the Medical College of Ohio. As John P. Foote noted, a history of its travails can well be called "a history of the Thirty Years War." [16] The charter designated Drake as president of the school and provided for six chairs, with Drake given medical practice, the most important one. But the charter named only four professors: Drake, Slack, Rogers, and Samuel Brown of Philadelphia, professor-elect of anatomy. Brown never came to Cincinnati but took a better offer at Transylvania. The faculty of three was next reduced to two when Rogers and Drake squabbled. In February 1820, Drake and Slack voted to expel Rogers from the school. These events postponed the opening of the school until the fall of 1820.

Rogers' falling-out with Drake was probably due to his chagrin at Drake's engrossment of nearly every office of importance in the school. Many local physicians were coming to a similar realization about Drake. Like Rogers they resented Drake's dominant position in Cincinnati medical circles. Drake was, after all, a newcomer with no preemptive claim to eminence among his fellows. Yet he had stolen the march on all of them and now reaped a harvest of jealousy and invective.

Early in 1820 a succession of vitriolic open letters appeared in the Cincinnati press. Drake was partly responsible for this when he publicly intimated the existence of a conspiracy against him and his school. His antagonists were organized in the Cincinnati Medical Society, a small private club, but the challenge was taken up by a nonmember, John Moorhead, an Irish immigrant physician. Moorhead assailed Drake in a series of epistles bordering on incoherency. Moorhead's formal purpose was to inquire whether Drake numbered him among the alleged conspirators. Drake's anwer was not long delayed, a delightful exhibition of repartee in the form of thirty-nine questions. Drake wondered "whether the Doctor's proclamation

16. John P. Foote, *The Schools of Cincinnati; And its Vicinity* (Cincinnati, 1855), p. 141.

would not be still less intelligible if read backwards or crosswise." He called attention to Moorhead's dubious scientific credentials and accused him of having spent the previous summer constructing, with predictable results, a perpetual-motion machine. He replied to Moorhead's insinuation that Drake was a backwoodsman with some innuendo of his own about Moorhead's Irish antecedents.[17]

Out of this parade of insults and witticisms certain truths emerged. For all his fulmination Moorhead unwittingly gave away his case by acknowledging:

> I have hitherto been amongst the number of those, who have regarded as altogether visionary your ambitious project of establishing and heading in this place a Medical College.[18]

The wild and visionary plan for the medical school was to Moorhead only another sign of Drake's instinct for self-aggrandizement. He conceded that among friends he laughed at Drake's project. In all likelihood he did more than laugh. The fierce tone of his letters indicates that Drake's suggestion of a conspiracy was not far wide of the mark. The plan for a medical school might have been visionary in 1818 but, supported by a charter, the project merited more than ridicule. Moorhead and other local physicians were anguished by much more than the thought of a fellow-townsman pursuing a chimera. A successful medical school would mean a rise in the number of doctors in the city and a consequent decline in patronage of the established ones.[19]

With Rogers' resignation and intensifying local opposition, Drake's prospects appeared gloomy, but he quickly mastered the situation. In August 1820 he announced a reorganization of the faculty. Benjamin Bohrer, a medical graduate of Pennsylvania, and Jesse Smith of Harvard came into the school to teach materia medica, and anatomy and surgery respectively. Classes began in the fall of 1820, and in January 1821 Drake induced the legislature to establish the Commercial Hospital and Lunatic Asylum at Cincinnati,

17. *The Western Spy*, Jan. 8, 15, 22, 1820; *Liberty Hall and Cincinnati Gazette*, Feb. 4, 11, 1820.

18. *The Western Spy*, Jan. 8, 1820.

19. Daniel Drake, *A Narrative of the Rise and Fall of the Medical College of Ohio* (Cincinnati, 1822), p. 18.

thus securing clinical facilities. A few months later he completed the reorganization by relinquishing physiology (which he had taught as part of medical practice) to Smith, who in turn relinquished surgery and obstetrics to John Godman, a recent medical graduate of the University of Maryland. Drake still generated the school's motion, but his responsibilities were trimmed.

While desirable on scientific grounds, the reorganization only nurtured jealousies. Shortly after the close of the 1822 school session Drake began to hear from professors Smith, Slack, and Bohrer "many oracular sayings concerning the state and prospects of the institution, from which it appeared that they were displeased with me." In the spring of 1822 Bohrer and Godman resigned, Bohrer because of antipathy to Drake and Godman because of antipathy to Smith, Slack, and Bohrer. Then, at a seriocomic faculty meeting in March, Smith and Slack expelled Drake from his own school.[20]

The same combination of wounded feelings and jealousies that impelled Moorhead to abuse Drake motivated the expulsion. Drake's antagonists were lesser men and probably knew it. Slack in particular was notoriously inept.[21] Both he and Smith resented Drake's control over the institution, especially since Drake no longer did most of the lecturing. Slack's feelings of inadequacy seemed to have produced an almost obsessive fear of Drake. He was certain that Drake was fomenting a student rebellion against him at Cincinnati College.[22] Bohrer was in league with Smith and Slack. He wanted the medical practice chair held by Drake, always the jewel in American medical schools, and Drake's refusal to relinquish the chair was the principal cause of Bohrer's resignation.

Drake's expulsion, however, was partly his own fault. The charge of conceit was so frequently leveled at him that it must have had

20. Ibid., pp. 9–11.
21. Slack had no training as a physician though some as a scientist. He was embarrassed by the superior dexterity of his assistant, Robert Best; see Horine, *Daniel Drake*, p. 172. For a sketch of Best, whose early death cut short a promising career, see "Biographia Medica," *West J. Med. Phys. Sciences, 4* (Jan.–March 1831) , 596–603.
22. Drake denied this and was supported by the trustees of Cincinnati College. Dr. Drake to Messrs. Howell, Lytle, James and Wilson, Lytle Family Papers, Box 24, no. 90, n.d.; George Wilson to Elijah Slack, March 11, 1822, ibid., Box 14, no. 57. The Lytle Papers and the Lytle Family Papers are in the Cincinnati Historical Society, hereafter CHS.

some basis in truth. Harriet Beecher Stowe noted in later years that Drake's bedside manner was that of a minister preaching a sermon on the doctrine of election. He recognized his superiority to his contemporaries and doubtless impressed them with it. Moreover, his ambition had led him to establish a proprietary school in the first place, and in 1822 he reaped a bitter and unanticipated harvest. Without effective outside control, appointments and dismissals rested with the faculty alone. Drake was safe only as long as he could command a majority among his fellow professors.

Drake's expulsion was followed by some complicated maneuvering which on the negative side resulted in further exacerbation of feelings and on the positive side led finally to creation of a state-appointed board of trustees.[23] Although he had a good deal of support among students and laymen and probably could have forced his way back into the school, Drake chose to accept a chair at Transylvania University, then the best medical school in the West. Smith and Slack carried on the Medical College on an attenuated basis. A few new professors joined the faculty, including C. E. Pierson of New York, two New Englanders, Jedidiah Cobb and Josiah Whitman, and Drake's nemesis Moorhead, who suddenly found the school a less wild and visionary scheme than in 1820. Cobb was the only really capable professor, and he was no Drake. The first skirmish of the war had definitely been a Malplaquet. Cincinnati lost its most gifted medical scientist and saw its medical school doomed to a subsidiary position behind Transylvania for a decade.

Harmony prevailed as long as Drake was out of the city. At Transylvania he eventually rose to the medical practice chair. But Lexington's days as Athens of the West were numbered. Lack of access to water routes put it at an economic disadvantage to Cincinnati, and Transylvania began its decline in 1827 when sectarian opposition forced the resignation of its dynamic Unitarian president, Horace

23. Public pressure forced Smith and Slack to ask Drake to return but Drake refused. Between 1822 and 1825 a series of laws virtually transformed the Medical College of Ohio into a state institution. See *Acts of Ohio,* 20 ass. (1822), ch. 3; 23 ass. (1824), pp. 19–20; 24 ass. (1826), pp. 4–8. In the original charter the faculty was made the body politic. According to the final law above, the trustees became the incorporated unit and no professor could be a trustee. The trustees had full power over appointments. See also Jesse Smith to Mr. and Mrs. Jonathan Bailey, April 29, 1823, CHS; Drake, *Rise and Fall of the Medical College of Ohio,* pp. 12–13.

Holley. Drake returned to Cincinnati and threw himself into civic and scientific work, launching an eye infirmary and assuming the editorship of the *Western Journal of the Medical and Physical Sciences.* In 1830 he spent a term as professor at Jefferson Medical College in Philadelphia, principally to recruit a teaching staff for a new assault on the Medical College of Ohio.

While Drake was in Philadelphia his brother Benjamin was convincing the trustees of Miami University in Oxford, Ohio, to authorize a medical faculty. The Miami faculty was to have six professors. Besides Drake, who had taken care to have himself made dean and professor of medical practice, there were James Staughton, surgery; John F. Henry, obstetrics; John Eberle, materia medica and botany; and Thomas D. Mitchell, pharmacy. Drake's brother-in-law Joseph N. McDowell, the nephew of Ephraim McDowell, was to take anatomy and physiology. The new faculty was about equally divided between Easterners and border-state men; only McDowell had a degree from a western medical school. The faculty of the Medical College witnessed the importation of heavy artillery from the East with dismay. Even without Drake the Miami faculty could rival the Medical College, and with Drake it was no contest. The Medical College faced the extinction it had long courted.

The trustees of the Medical College averted disaster by engineering a rather brutal reorganization that resembled a game of musical chairs. Slack and Smith were forced out of the school and Whitman resigned. The trustees then created a new chair in medical jurisprudence and gave it to C. E. Pierson, hitherto the professor of materia medica. Next they lured away three of Drake's Miami associates—Mitchell, Staughton, and Eberle—with offers of positions in the Medical College. Mitchell became professor of chemistry; Staughton took the surgery post and became dean of the faculty; Eberle, next to Drake the ablest of the Miami professors, was given materia medica and botany. This maneuver isolated Drake and reduced his bargaining power. His only ally was Henry. Drake could have recruited a new faculty and tried again, but it was unlikely that in a short time he could match the galaxy of luminaries he had assembled at Miami. Instead, he chose somewhat humbly to ask for a chair in the Medical College. He insisted that some kind of accommodation be made for Henry. The trustees preferred to have Drake in a minor post within the college than plotting mischief outside and hence offered him a newly created chair in clinical medicine and Henry a chair in obstetrics. Moorhead held onto the medical practice chair.[24]

Events did not reward the contrivers of this ingenious reorganization. In January 1832 Drake resigned. Staughton, Mitchell, and Eberle had consistently sided with Moorhead in faculty councils. Drake seemed destined to be outvoted in every issue, and one issue was vital to him. Accustomed to being first among equals, Drake had had to settle for the clinical medicine chair, a minor post in the thirties with scarcely enough student interest to sustain a professor. His only hope was to force the trustees to unite his chair with Pierson's chair in medical jurisprudence and to banish Pierson. Drake's arguments were reasonable. Pierson had asked for and received a year's leave to prepare himself in New York for lecturing on medical jurisprudence. In his absence Drake lectured informally and successfully on Pierson's subject. He assumed that Pierson's virtual confession of incompetence would persuade the trustees to favor him. When it did not, Drake left. In Ohio medical politics of the thirties Drake's departure meant an automatic sentence of expulsion for his friend Henry, a formality carried out in April 1832 by the elimination of Henry's chair.

From April 1832 to 1835 Cincinnati's presses were kept busy turning out a cavalcade of pamphlets and broadsides as each side sought to justify its conduct. Henry started this protracted postmortem with *An Exposure of the Conduct of the Trustees and Professors of the Medical College of Ohio, and of the Hospital and Township Trustees.*[25] Henry protested that he had been charged with incompetence when his only real sin was affection for Drake. He insisted that the faculty, board of trustees, and Township Trustees (Cincinnati officials entrusted with oversight of certain public projects including the Commercial Hospital) were in collusion, that he and Drake were victims of a conspiracy (pp. 10–15).

Drake soon buttressed his friend's case. A memorandum to the legislature, signed by officials of the Third District Medical Society

24. "Medical College of Ohio," *West. J. Med. Phys. Sciences,* 7 (April 1, 1834), 624–27; "Report of Commissioners to visit the Medical College of Ohio . . . *Ohio Senate J.,* 32 leg. (1833), pp. 220–22; *Cincinnati Daily Gazette,* Feb. 18, 1832.

25. Cincinnati, 1832.

at Xenia but instigated by Drake, assailed the management of the Medical College of Ohio. Drake's instinct for the jugular led him to Professor Pierson and a trustee, Daniel Gano. Pierson, a native New Yorker who had never become an official resident of Ohio, had in effect acknowledged his unfitness for the jurisprudence chair by asking for a year's leave for preparation. Moreover, Drake was not blind to the sinister motive behind the trustees' willingness to placate Pierson. Pierson's brother-in-law was Samuel Davies, a trustee and after 1833 the mayor of Cincinnati. Gano was an even more vulnerable target. A notorious eccentric, he had long been a true believer in Thomsonianism.[26] The charges of nepotism against Davies and Thomsonianism against Gano were among Drake's more potent weapons throughout the controversy.

The trustees stated their case with equal force. Bringing Drake into the college, their argument ran, was an act of largess. Once in, he had no right to dictate the composition of the faculty. They accused Drake of haranguing his classes against them and with discouraging students from coming to Cincinnati so long as the college was under its present management. Ignoring the welfare of the institution, and wanting only scope for his exertions, a theater for his talents, he had nearly wrecked the college once and now was bent on doing it again.[27]

The usual complement of innuendo and pettiness that will forever mark Drake's foes as smaller men, however, accompanied their substantial arguments. They ridiculed Drake for making himself a virtual surgeon-general of Cincinnati during the 1832 cholera epidemic. Drake had indeed issued public warnings and advice during the epidemic, but only because his opponents insisted that the epidemic would be mild, which it was not, or was only an outbreak of marsh fever, which it was not. Drake deserved more for his efforts than carping, but he did not receive it from his contemporaries. Perhaps the low point in the whole controversy was the publication of the "Vindex" letters, written by Alban G. Smith, professor of surgery at the Medical College, and published in the *Cincinnati Whig and Commerical Intelligencer* during the summer of 1835.

26. Diary of Major Daniel Gano. MS, CHS. Despite its title this is really an autobiography written in the third person.

27. "Memorial of Trustees of the Medical College of Ohio," *Ohio House J.*, 31 ass. (1832) , Jan. 14, 1832, p. 253.

Smith's vilification of Drake was personal, only semicoherent, and often wildly distorted. It was a bad performance, below par even for Drake's antagonists.[28]

The pamphlet war occasioned by Drake's resignation led to a legislative investigation of the college in 1835. The results were inconclusive; Drake's charges against the old board of trustees were not sustained, but new trustees were elected anyway. Perhaps the main effect of the controversy was to obfuscate issues originally fairly simple. Drake in 1832 had found himself in roughly the same position of Benjamin Bohrer ten years previously. He coveted a chair beyond his reach. Like Bohrer he left, hoping to return when a more favorable climate prevailed. His enemies charged him with base motives, but he was only playing the game according to the rules of the day. His sole regret was that he lost, but again, given the extraordinary fickleness of whatever goddess presided over professional fortunes in the 1830s, his prospects for reestablishing himself as the city's leading lecturer appeared to be excellent. People who had some profession other than teaching medicine esteemed him, and the pamphlet war had not tarnished his reputation as a polemicist.

In the normal course one would have expected Drake to start a rival college in Cincinnati. One could also expect, considering Drake's talents, that he would succeed. Had this happened, the experience of other states would have been duplicated, and for a time Drake's success seemed certain. The third and final phase of the war began in 1835, when Drake announced the establishment of a medical department at Cincinnati College. In view of the remarkable scope of Cincinnati College's original charter there was no legal difficulty in this. Drake's new faculty was superior to that of the Medical College. It included Samuel Gross, shortly to publish a classic work on pathological anatomy; John Pollard, destined to become a noted author on materia medica; and Willard Parker, one of the finest surgeons of his day.[29] By its second session, 1836–37,

28. Smith's diatribe was published anonymously as *An Inquiry into the Causes that have Retarded the Prosperity of the Medical College of Ohio* (Cincinnati, 1835). Smith got his just desserts from Drake in Drake's *Medical Department of Cincinnati College to the Public* (Cincinnati, 1835).

29. The faculty also included James B. Rogers, professor of chemistry and brother of William Barton Rogers, the founder of the Massachusetts Institute of Technology; Landon Rives, a Virginian; and John L. Riddell.

the enrollment at Cincinnati's medical department rivaled the Medical College's. Drake's relations with his fellow professors were for once cordial. The omens were favorable.

Victory, however, once again eluded Drake's grasp. The medical department of Cincinnati College collapsed in 1839 with a mass of resignations. Internal wrangling was not the cause, nor have the causes been adequately explored by historians. The Panic of 1837 and the opening of the Louisville Medical Institute in 1838 undoubtedly hurt Drake's department. But he had started the Medical College of Ohio in the middle of one financial recession; he could have kept Cincinnati's department going despite another recession. As for the rival in Louisville, the presence of competition had never bothered Drake before. Louisville threatened the Medical College more than it did him.

The insurmountable problem for Drake was lack of access to clinical facilities. The Medical College monopolized wards of the Commerical Hospital and Lunatic Asylum, ironically one of Drake's creations. For a while his students used the eye infirmary, which he had started in the late twenties, and a marine hospital built next to the Cincinnati College by the United States government. But the eye infirmary was too small, and local officials refused to send sick boatmen to the marine hospital.[30] Local officials also blocked Drake's final plan. In February 1839 the legislature voted to give the Township Trustees permission to admit Drake's students to the Commercial Hospital, but the trustees consistently refused to do so.

Without clinical facilities even Drake could not attract students. By 1839 his department was doomed. But Drake's failure to gain facilities raises some significant questions. Why did the legislature authorize the Township Trustees to admit his students? Why did the Township Trustees refuse? Were there outside forces at work in the medical "war"?

Contemporary accounts fail to do justice to the complexity of the issue. Drake's party talked of alleged mismanagement in the Commercial Hospital. His opponents retorted with charges of Drake's

---

30. *Cincinnati Advertiser and Western Journal,* Feb. 1, 4, 1839. Drake also proposed having the eye infirmary attached to the Commercial Hospital. He somewhat disingenuously stressed the public utility of this. His real goal was to gain admission to the hospital for his students.

own inattention to the hospital while he was professor of clinical medicine at the Medical College in the early thirties.[31] In fact, the "war of extermination" between the Medical College of Ohio and the medical department of Cincinnati College in the late thirties divided Cincinnati into rival factions not because of conflicting evaluations of the state of the hospital but for reasons unrelated to medical science or to the techniques of hospital management.

Drake's principal attachment had always been to the party of Daniel Drake. But in the early thirties he began to see how the emergence of Jacksonian and Whig parties out of the old National Republican coalition could be of value to him. His own political principles were Whiggish. Drake was a noted publicist of internal improvements and a staunch friend of Henry Clay, the architect of the American System. Drake's brother Benjamin, who agreed with Daniel on most issues, attacked Jackson for his war on the Bank of the United States. Daniel Drake was, moreover, an ardent temperance man, an issue which attracted considerable local Whig support.[32] But Drake's ambition to control the Medical College of Ohio led him away from a Whig allegiance. Most of the trustees of the college were prominent Whigs. Samuel Davies, mayor after 1833, was the leading Whig politician in the city. Few trustees sided more relentlessly with Drake's opponents in the faculty than Bellamy Storer and United States Senator Jacob Burnet, both leading Whigs. Late in 1834, after his resignation and while searching for a new entrance route to the college, Drake wrote to Robert Todd Lytle, Ohio Congressmen and one of the ablest figures in the Democratic party, to solicit Lytle's support in the election of new trustees of the Medical College. Drake noted that,

> Our friends Burnet and Storer are up there [Columbus], no doubt to secure their reappointment as trustees of the Medical College, and will rely no doubt on the old story of

31. Some important documents are reprinted in [Joseph Bonsall], *Controversy in Relation to the Medical Schools of Ohio* . . . (Cincinnati, 1839); see also Daniel Drake, *The War of Extermination* (Cincinnati, 1839).

32. Daniel Drake, *A Discourse on Intemperance* (Cincinnati, 1828). In 1852 Drake wrote a number of interesting letters to John C. Warren on slavery. Drake's position was conservative, though not archly so, and fairly typical of border-state thinking at the time. See Daniel Drake, *Letters on Slavery to Dr. John C. Warren of Boston* . . . , introduction by Emmet F. Horine, M.D. (New York, 1940).

"Drake's hostility." I will thank you to send me a note of introduction to Gov. Lucas with whom I am not acquainted. . . .

A large majority of the Board are now of one political party. If you think reform necessary, a line from you to some of your friends in the Legislature might do much good. Your influence with Anderson of this county would be great and beneficial, but if you write to him, do not mention either my name or Moorhead's.[33]

In fact nearly all the trustees were Whigs, and this remained true even after the election of new ones in 1835. Because they blocked Drake's path, he cast his lot with the Jacksonians.

On the surface this was a wise move. Ohio returned for Jackson in 1832 and had a Democratic governor from 1832 to 1836. Democratic forces increasingly dominated the Ohio legislature. But to achieve his ends Drake needed support from local officials. He hoped that the Democrats would soon sweep out Davies and the conservative Whig oligarchy that controlled the city. Here, however, his plans met frustration. While Ohio went Democratic, Cincinnati remained under Whig dominance until the mid-1840s.

Drake's efforts to secure clinical facilities for the medical department of Cincinnati College illustrated the effects of these conflicting political movements. As a friend of the Van Buren administration he easily secured the aid of local Jackson notables to obtain a federal endowment for the marine hospital connected with Cincinnati College.[34] When he recognized the inadequacy of the marine hospital he turned to his friends in the Ohio legislature for authorization to admit his students to the Commerical Hospital. The bills to authorize the Township Trustees to admit Drake's students passed with Democratic support over considerable Whig opposition.[35] But the refusal of the Township Trustees to admit his students blocked his plans. Here again the motivation was political. The Township

33. Daniel Drake to Robert Todd Lytle, Dec. 17, 1834. MS, Lytle Papers, Box 24, no. 91, CHS.

34. [Joseph Bonsall], *Controversy in Relation to the Medical Schools of Ohio* . . . (Cincinnati, 1839), p. 7. Bonsall was a Whig politician of no particular importance.

35. *Ohio House J.*, 37 ass. (1838), Feb. 19, 1839, p. 507, for yeas and nays. Party affiliations are listed in the *Cincinnati Daily Whig*, Oct. 30, 1838.

Trustees elected in 1838 were Josiah Fobes, Thatcher Lewis, and William Crossman. All were Whigs and all had come out publicly against admission of Drake's students. The Jacksonian candidates, all favoring admission, were so soundly defeated that Drake must have abandoned all hope of securing a more favorable political climate in Cincinnati. In this calculation he was right. Fobes, Lewis, and Crossman were returned with solid majorities well into the forties, until the growing stridency of local abolitionism disrupted Cincinnati's Whigs. By that time Drake was teaching at the Louisville Medical Institute.[36] Once again Kentucky had profited from the twists and turns of Cincinnati's medical politics.

The absence of an established professional hierarchy only aggravated rivalries in Ohio. Compared with the hyperacidity of the Ohio profession, antagonisms elsewhere were carried on in an almost courtly manner. The spectacle of members of a liberal and disinterested profession denouncing each other's qualifications and character in newspapers plunged physicians into public disesteem. By 1837 the Medical College of Ohio had become a standing joke within the profession. *The Boston Medical and Surgical Journal* called it "an apparently rotten institution." [37] Few reputable teachers would seriously consider going there.

Moreover, when rival professional factions entered politics they always ran the risk of retaliatory legislation. In 1833, when the licensing law was repealed, the legislature also struck out the legal basis of the district societies. Drake and others recognized that the legislature had gone farther than the profession had hoped. A removal of penalties on unlicensed practice would have satisfied all parties, but elimination of the incorporated status of the societies seemed a vindictive blow at the profession.

36. Drake returned to the Medical College in 1849 when he was nearly 65. He taught there until his death in 1852. A number of factors motivated his return. Moorhead had gone back to Ireland, there was a slot for him at the Medical College, and he wanted to see his classic work, *A Systematic Treatise . . . on the Principal Diseases of the Interior Valley of North America*, through the presses. See Horine, *Daniel Drake*, ch. 17. No serious rival to the Medical College appeared between 1839 and 1850. A few mild challenges arose from 1850 to 1860. See William F. Norwood, *Medical Education in the United States before the Civil War* (Philadelphia, 1944), pp. 321–24.

37. Quoted in Otto Juettner, *Daniel Drake and His Followers: Historical and Biographical Sketches* (Cincinnati, 1909), p. 145.

The explanation for this lies partly in the unsatisfactory performance of the district societies. Many of the societies were not functioning at all. Attendance in others was spotty, and meetings generated nothing of scientific value. But some of the district societies were extremely active, not in the cause of science but in factional intrigue. The faculty of the Medical College of Ohio controlled the First District Society in Cincinnati. Either shortly before or after his removal from the college John F. Henry ran for president of the society, but lost to an anti-Drake candidate. Henry and the remainder of Drake's supporters formed a rival Cincinnati Medical Society. Drake also worked through the Third District Society. Its memorial attacking the trustees of the Medical College in 1833 was largely his work. The signers in fact represented only themselves. Few members of the Third District Society knew anything at all about the memorial until its publication—it was not even printed in Xenia but in Cincinnati. Drake was obviously using a medical society as an aegis to advance his own interests. The fact that the district societies lost their incorporated status in the same year that a crisis was reached in the affairs of the Medical College of Ohio was more than a coincidence. The memorial that called for a state licensing board also sought radical changes in the Medical College. A legislator who candidly viewed the matter in 1833 would hardly be blamed for concluding that, if the only function of the district societies was to shield rival factions competing for medical chairs, then the state was better off without them.

THE PERILS OF CONTROL

Both Massachusetts and Ohio achieved a degree of institutional control over medical education, with notably different results. In Massachusetts the coalition between Harvard and the leadership of the medical society checked proliferation, a desirable goal since multiplication of the number of medical schools in the commonwealth would have lowered the quality of education. Harvard had one of the finest medical faculties in the nation. Unable to match Harvard's facilities, a rival school would have had to offer a quick, cheap education as an inducement to matriculation.

The Ohio example, however, presents a very different picture of institutional control. While the proprietary character of the Medical

College of Ohio caused many of its early trials, the school remained the scene of periodic bloodlettings between rival factions even after the appointment of a state board of trustees in the mid-twenties. Though state control provided a way of settling disputes, it was no guarantee of harmony, and the manner in which the disputes were ultimately quieted—the expulsion of Daniel Drake—damaged the profession. The Medical College of Ohio beat off its founder, sometime professor, and perennial rival at a great price. Drake was the most distinguished scientist and teacher in the state; his departure for Louisville in 1839 was a serious blow to Ohio.

Ohio, then, offers another perspective on institutional control. As long as medical schools had strong ties to state governments or universities they could intrigue against the establishment of rivals. In some older states like Massachusetts this was an advantage; the faculties of the earliest medical schools in the nation could often boast of noted scientists trained in the finest European universities. But in a new state like Ohio no such hierarchy existed. Everyone was a newcomer; no one could claim superlative credentials. The original faculty of the Medical College was a chance assemblage that included a luminary (Drake), a mediocrity (Smith), and a nonentity (Slack). After the state assumed direction of the college all the professors were mediocre. The effect of state control was to put a ceiling on an already low level of faculty attainment. A successful rival school under Drake's control would have improved the quality of medical education in the state, and had the Medical College been proprietary in the 1830s Drake would never have encountered the harassment from local officials that ruined his plans to found a rival school.

Even in older states tighter control over medical education was not always a blessing. In Maryland, for example, the attempt by a state board of trustees to harness the previously unrestrained activities of the medical faculty of the "University of Maryland" led to unhappy results. When the trustees launched a faculty to rival the original regents' faculty, they nominated local mediocrities. The regents' faculty in contrast included nationally known figures like Robley Dunglison and Eli Geddings. The effect of state control was to force Dunglison and Geddings to quit Baltimore in frustration.

A principal cause of the failure of the Medical College of South

Carolina in its struggle with Dickson's Medical College of the State of South Carolina was that the former school brought in professors from the North while the latter state-controlled institution restricted its faculty to local products. Precisely because state governments were more susceptible to local pressures, they were less likely to import nationally renowned professors.

In semifrontier states like Ohio, however, these factors took on new urgency. Maryland was an exception among older states in its failure to produce local physicians with national reputations. In South Carolina the state institution, though its faculty was composed only of Southerners, had its share of medical luminaries. States like New York and Massachusetts had little need to go beyond their borders to recruit talented and renowned professors. But in Ohio the cause of quality in medical education would have been best served by a relatively free policy, by a willingness to look anywhere for able teachers. State control discouraged this kind of recruitment policy while private control encouraged it.

For all its defects, the proprietary school fitted the impatience with restraint that marked the temper of Jacksonian America. It was a product of its times and met the needs of a relatively unformed society. Tighter control over medical education made sense in some older states but could be a brake to quality in the large areas of the country emerging from the frontier phase of development between 1800 and 1860.

FOUR

Samuel Thomson and the Rise of
Sectarian Medicine

April 1, 1729:   *Order'd William Allen of Brigend blooded for the*
                  Pleurisie.

April 2:   *Ordered him blooded again.*

April 3:   *He was blooded again, 10 ounces being taken away*
                  as before.

April 4:   *He dyed.*

The Diary of Benjamin Rogers, Eighteenth-century Rector of Carlton,
England.

The mature deliberation of men of good will, the framers of regulatory legislation assumed, would arrive at a distinction between educated physicians on the one hand and empirics and quacks on the
other. The "mere empiric," unlike the educated physician, had no
philosophy of cure save that of hit or miss. An empiric who exaggerated his success dropped into the category of quack, a charlatan
out to bilk the public. Americans had been introduced to quackery
as early as 1630 when Nicholas Knopp of Massachusetts was fined
five pounds and whipped for vending as a cure for scurvy "a water
of no worth or value," which he "solde att a very deare rate." [1] The
careers of Elisha Perkins and his son, Benjamin Douglas Perkins,
provided examples of all three concepts.

Born in Norwich, Connecticut, in 1741, Elisha Perkins began
to practice medicine in 1759. During the next thirty-five years he
built up a large practice but had to supplement his income with an
active mule-breeding and trading business. In 1795, perhaps influenced by the experiments of Galvani on the production of muscu-

1. *Records of the Governor and Company of the Massachusetts Bay in New England*
(Boston, 1853), *1*, 83.

lar contractions through the contact of metals with living fiber, Perkins began a course of experiments resulting in the apparent discovery of the remedial value of drawing a knife blade over a painful area. Perkins became convinced that inflammatory and rheumatic pains were due to an excess of electricity in the part, which could be drawn off by the blade. His first public declaration of his findings was greeted with some enthusiasm by the profession, but less favorable winds were soon to blow from that direction. In 1796 Perkins, having decided to exploit the pecuniary possibilities of his discovery, secured a patent for metallic tractors which he sold for twenty-five dollars a pair. Perkins admitted that the tractors were no more effective than a knife blade, but they gave an air of mystery to findings, which convinced the gullible. In the following year Perkins was expelled from the Connecticut Medical Society for using a secret remedy. For all his Yankee shrewdness, however, Perkins sincerely viewed himself as a benefactor of mankind. When yellow fever broke out in New York in 1799, Perkins journeyed to the city to prove the worth of his treatment. While this attested to his sincerity, it proved fatal in other respects. Stricken with the fever, Perkins died shortly after his arrival.[2]

If lacking his father's inventive turn of mind, Benjamin Douglas Perkins far surpassed him as a publicist. Sensing that America had seen enough of the tractors, Benjamin took ship for England where he met Thomas Green Fessenden, a sometime Yankee mechanic, lawyer, poet, and, later, editor of the *New England Farmer*. The impecunious Fessenden was easily persuaded to expound the virtues of the tractors in verse, and in 1803 the first edition of *Terrible Tractoration!!* was published. Fessenden's protagonist, Christopher Caustic, was an orthodox physician enraged and impoverished by competition from the tractors:

> But now, alas! a wicked wag
> Has pull'd away the gaseous bag

2. Jacques M. Quen, "Elisha Perkins, Physician, Nostrum-Vendor, or Charlatan," *Bull. Hist. Med.*, 37 (March–April 1963), 159–66; Oliver Wendell Holmes, "Homoeopathy and Its Kindred Delusions," in *Medical Essays: 1842–1882, 9* in Writings of Oliver Wendell Holmes (Boston, 1891), 15–39; James Harvey Young, *The Toadstool Millionaires: A Social History of Patent Medicines in America before Federal Regulation* (Princeton, 1961), pp. 21–27; see also *J. Hist. Med., 19* (July 1964), 296–97.

> From heaven, where thron'd like Jove I sat
> I'm fall'n! fall'n! fall'n! down
> flat! flat! flat!

As for the tractors:

> As time rolls on, with raptur'd eye, behold
> The laws of nature constantly unfold!
> Behold Galvani's vivid, viewless flame,
> Bids mimick life, resuscitate the frame
> Of man deceas'd;—the vital lamp to burn
> With transitory glow, in death's cold win.
> See POINTED METALS, blest with power t'appease,
> The ruthless rage of merciless disease,
> O'er the frail part a subtle fluid pour,
> Drench'd with invisible Galvanick shower,
> Till the arthritick staff and crutch forego,
> And leap exulting like the bounding roe! [3]

Despite its semicomical style, *Terrible Tractoration!!* drew the interest of many a solemn Doctor of Divinity to the tractors, and endorsements from on high were soon forthcoming. Though one clergyman could not explain why "the waters of Jordan should be better than Abana and Pharpar, rivers of Damascus," he had witnessed the success of the tractors in his own family and, what experience has proved, "no reasoning can change the opinion." [4] The tractors were especially popular with English ladies. Through female influence the tractors were conveyed to Denmark where they became the ruling passion. For Benjamin Perkins, however, the Old World had already served its purpose. He returned to America, richer by £10,000, to pass his declining years as a gentleman bookseller and philanthropist in New York City.

Though Oliver Wendell Holmes in 1842 classified it as a delusion akin to homoeopathy, Perkinism was of a different species. Elisha Perkins himself was a queer amalgam of educated physician and charlatan, genuinely believing he had made a major scientific discovery but willing to distort its nature for profit. But, although the

3. Thomas G. Fessenden (Christopher Caustic, pseud.) *The Modern Philosopher; or Terrible Tractoration!!* (2d Amer. ed. Philadelphia, 1806), pp. xxxi, 17.
4. Holmes, "Homoeopathy and Its Kindred Delusions," pp. 25ff.

tractors won scores of admirers, Perkinism never became a medical sect; it lacked a coherent medical theory applicable to all ailments. The tractors were useful only for localized aches and pains, and fascination always focused more on the tractors than on any explanation Perkins offered for their alleged success. Elisha Perkins died without developing a medical system with broad scientific, philosophical, and social implications, and his son was far more interested in profits than pathology. Perkinism's true ancestors were the King's Touch and Bishop Berkeley's Tar Water; its descendants were the great nostrum-mongers of the nineteenth century: Thomas Dyott, William Swaim, and Benjamin Brandreth. In the thirties and forties regulatory laws were confronted and destroyed by a new type of medical creed. Botanic doctors (Thomsonian, neo-Thomsonian, and Eclectic) and homoeopaths were possessed of organizations and bodies of doctrine which rendered their description by any traditional concept—educated physician, quack, or empiric—highly dubious. In addition to illustrating the types of people most inclined to support irregular medical movements, Perkinism serves as a useful contrast to these later medical crusades.

THE RISE OF THOMSONIANISM

For the facts of Samuel Thomson's life we have only to consult his autobiography.[5] Engaged in a pursuit of "more consequence to the great human family, than any other that could be undertaken by man; that of alleviating human misery, by curing all cases of disease by the most simple, safe and certain method of practice," Thomson recorded the details of his life, and especially childhood, with a thoroughness suggesting an extraordinary sense of mission (p. 13). An enthusiastic follower later claimed that "Thomsonism is the cause of humanity." Samuel Thomson had reached that conclusion before he was thirty.

Thomson was born in 1769 in Alstead, New Hampshire, the scion of strict Baptists. Though lame, he went to work in the fields with his father when he was less than four years old. "I was very curious," he related, "to know the names of all the herbs which I saw growing,

5. Samuel Thomson, *New Guide to Health; or Botanic Family Physician . . . to which is prefixed, A Narrative of the Life and Medical Discoveries of the Author* (2d ed. Boston, 1825).

and what they were good for." A local female herbal practitioner took the youth on her field trips, and from her Thomson learned the names of many common plants (pp. 16–19).

By his own account Thomson made his major discovery at the age of four when, out of curiosity, he began to chew one of the plants which had previously escaped his attention. The taste was so remarkable that he never forgot it. The plant was *lobelia inflata,* a common emetic, and Thomson delighted in inducing other boys to chew it, "merely by way of sport, to see them vomit (p. 16). For a number of years he continued his life on the farm, experimenting on himself and others, but never attempting to formulate a medical theory.

When in his twenties, Thomson tested his emetic again, this time on a farm laborer. The usual vomiting resulted, but on this occasion it was followed by a rapid improvement in health, and the man felt better than he had for a long time (p. 27). His success led Thomson to conclude that he possessed "a gift in healing the sick," and, inconsistently, to formulate a theoretical explanation for the remedial powers of lobelia (p. 40).

After considering the subject, Thomson decided that all animal bodies were formed of four elements: earth, fire, air, and water. "Earth and water constitute the solids, and air and fire, or heat, are the cause of life and motion." Disease was invariably due to the lessening of heat. Treatment commenced with steam baths—"until the sweat rolls off as thick as your finger"—designed to render the patient more receptive to the following steps: the natural heat of the body was promoted either directly, by use of "hot" botanicals like red peppers, or indirectly, through emetics, purgatives, and enemas. Though Thomson later expanded the number of botanicals to over sixty, lobelia always occupied the most prominent position in the botanic physician's medicine bag.[6]

Despite its crudity Thomson's system bore a notable resemblance to the pathology of John Brown of Edinburgh, which was accepted by most orthodox physicians in America. Brown differed from Thomson only in holding that, since moderation was the key to health, "excitability" could be as fatal as deficiency. Orthodox physicians

6. Philip D. Jordan, "The Secret Six, An Inquiry into the Basic Materia Medica of the Thomsonian System of Botanic Medicine," *Ohio State Archaeol. Hist. Quarterly,* 52 (Oct.–Dec. 1943), 350–52; Young, *Toadstool Millionaires,* pp. 46–47.

had pioneered advances in anatomy and physiology in the eighteenth century and were beginning to take an interest in clinical instruction, but pathology and therapeutics had taken few strides forward.

Although he possessed a system, Thomson still lacked a secure position. As he extended his practice beyond his Vermont homestead, reports of his cures reached the regular profession. Unlike Perkins, he belonged to no medical society, and, indeed, he had learned only the rudiments of grammar. Rumors were circulated that lobelia had killed some of his patients, and in 1809 he was arrested for murder in Salisbury, Massachusetts. Thomson's chief accuser was a regular physician named French. "I had very considerable practice in his neighborhood," Thomson wrote, "and thus seemed to excite his malice against me to the greatest pitch." [7] Thomson was not only a murderer, French alleged, but he practiced witchcraft as well. After spending a month in a foul jail, where his only companion was a convicted rapist, Thomson was brought to trial, appropriately at Salem. He had been summoned to treat a dying man, Thomson claimed, and had launched the patient toward recovery. But the patient left his bed too quickly and went out into the chill of a December day. A relapse followed, accompanied by delirium, and the patient soon expired. Prosecution witnesses had another version. Flaunting his lack of scientific knowledge by calling his herbs "ram-cats" and "well-my-gristle," Thomson had so heroically dosed his patient that death was a blessing. But at a key point in the trial Thomson called on Manasseh Cutler, the botanist, to testify that the plant alleged to be lobelia was in fact only marsh rosemary, a harmless if ineffective remedy. [8] To French's chagrin Thomson won aquittal.

The year 1809 was the turning point of Thomson's life. No longer content with the lot of a peripatetic herb doctor one step ahead of the sheriff, he again "maturely considered the subject in all its bearings," and concluded:

> There was only one plan for me to pursue with any chance
> of success; and that was to go on to Washington and ob-
> tain a patent for my discoveries; and put myself and medi-
> cine under the protection of the laws of my country,

7. Thomson, *Narrative*, p. 66.
8. *Commonwealth v. Samuel Thomson*, 6 Tyng, 134.

which would not only secure to me the exclusive right to my system and medicine, but would put me above the reach of the laws of any state.[9]

In 1813, taking advantage of the laxity of patent law which required proof of neither novelty nor utility, Thomson obtained a patent "signed by the *President, Secretary,* and *Attorney-General,* of the United States." [10] Armed with this document he set about forming laymen who paid twenty dollars for a right to his system into "friendly botanic societies" where members could discuss cures and exchange information. As he gathered a following, Thomson had occasion to hire managers to look after his interests in certain areas. The most interesting of these, because of his resemblance to Thomson and to a type of person who was to play a vital role in making "steamery" a mass movement, was Elias Smith.

Smith was born in 1769, the same year as Thomson, in Lyme, Connecticut. Seemingly insignificant details of his early life were of great interest to Smith in his later years, and his rambling and ponderous autobiography, *The Life, Conversion, Preaching, Travels and Sufferings of Elias Smith,* is posterity's evidence of this concern.[11] While Thomson's precocity was directed to the study of herbs, Smith's early enthusiasm was entirely religious. "Many times before I was eight years old," Smith later related, "I lay awake till late, thinking what would become of me, and sometimes wished that I had never existed; or that I had been any thing but an accountable creature" (p. 23). Smith's home life little distracted him from his religious concern; his father was a Baptist by profession and his mother a new light Congregationalist. Connecticut was the scene of many an "outpouring of the spirit" in Elias' youth, and attendance at numerous revivals started him on the path to conversion.

In 1782, after his family's removal to Woodstock, Vermont, Smith finally rid himself of "guilt, pollution, and condemnation" through baptism. With his mind fixed on scriptures it was not long before he became a wandering lay preacher (pp. 114–56). Other Baptists had warned him that "when I saw a man dressed in *black;* called *rever-*

---

9. Thomson, *Narrative,* pp. 12, 102–03.
10. Quoted in Young, *Toadstool Millionaires,* p. 51.
11. Boston, 1840. It was published as volume I of a projected two-volume work, but Smith died before he could fulfill his plan.

end; reading his notes; having a salary; taking property from others by force; and despising such as travelled and preached, etc. that such were the *devil's ministers,* and ought to be avoided" (p. 165). Smith's anticlericalism did not receive full elaboration until he settled in Woburn, Massachusetts, where a Commonwealth law required ordination for all preachers. Submitting initially with some reluctance, since "no such thing is mentioned in the Bible," Smith was soon beset by doubts about the legitimacy of ministerial associations to force payment of tithes, and further found himself "quite too respectable for a minister of Christ" (pp. 243–48). Concluding that the clergy in general were what the New Testament called anti-Christ, Smith removed to Portsmouth, New Hampshire, and began describing himself as a "Christian" after the manner of the followers of Alexander Campbell, calling no man father or master; holding as abominable in the sight of God everything highly esteemed among men (p. 299):

> such as calvinism, arminianism, freewillism, universalism, reverend, parsons, chaplains, doctors of divinity, clergy, covenants, platforms, with the spirit of slander which those who hold to these things are often in possession of.

For Elias Smith the road from enthusiasm to fanaticism had been short.

In 1816 Smith fell ill with "bilious cholic" while visiting Boston. Having been convinced for several years that vegetable remedies were the best, he applied to a Thomsonian doctor and found relief. At about the same time Samuel Thomson was looking for a suitable person as a general agent. Many characteristics of Elias Smith impressed Thomson as "suitable." Each had passed much of his life in Vermont and New Hampshire; each was raised in sectarian religious surroundings; each man felt possessed of a mission to loose the shackles that enslaved the common man, being convinced in Thompson's words, that the priest, the doctor, and the lawyer were deceiving the people.[12] Each had, in addition, the intolerance of the missionary, a quality not conducive to friendships. The phrenologist Orson Fowler later examined Thomson's skull and concluded that he was quick

12. Samuel Thomson, *New Guide to Health . . . to which is prefixed, A Narrative of the Life and Medical Discoveries of the Author* (Boston, 1835), p. 201. All other references are to the 1825 edition, unless explicitly noted.

to anger and "obstinate even to mulishness." Smith and Thomson soon quarreled bitterly, and much of the latter's *Narrative* is occupied with a tale of betrayal.[13]

Wooster Beach, the founder of Eclecticism, never wrote an autobiography, but he filled his medical treatises with details of his life. Beach was born in Trumbull, Connecticut, in 1794. Evincing an ardent passion for research, particularly in the fields of theology and medicine, he set about gathering information from old wives, root doctors, Indian doctors, and even orthodox physicians.[14] In the twenties Beach moved to New York where he joined the county medical society, established a hospital (modestly named the United States Infirmary) and worked out the tenets of Eclecticism. Eclectic or "reformed" medicine relied mainly on plant medicinals, substituting vegetable emetics such as *Leptandra virginica* for calomel, and gamboge, scammony, and colocynth for tarter emetic. But Eclectics were not above using "vegetable poisons" like opium, digitalis, and rhubarb which were denounced by orthodox Thomsonians, and mineral remedies when herbal substitutes were lacking.[15] While gathering material for his *summa, The American Practice of Medicine*,[16] Beach edited the *Telescope,* a journal devoted to radical religious and political causes, in whose pages he proclaimed against the four evils of the world: "King-craft, Priest-craft, Lawyer-craft, and Doctor-craft." His attachment to radicalism was continued in later years in his edit-

13. Thomson, *Narrative*, pp. 154–63. Thomson accused Smith of forming rival botanic societies and sued for trespass. Justice Story, however, upheld Smith on the ground that Thomson's original patent was too vague. Thomson was forced to secure a new patent, specifying that the novelty of his system lay in the proper ordering of the herbs, not in the herbs themselves.

14. Alexander Wilder, *History of Medicine: A Brief Outline of Medical History . . . and Especially a History of the American Eclectic Practice of Medicine, never before Published* (New Sharon, Me., 1901), p. 434; H. W. Felton, *History of the Eclectic Medical Institute, Cincinnati, Ohio: 1845–1902* (Cincinnati, 1902), p. 81.

15. Alex Berman, "The Impact of the Nineteenth Century Botanico-Medical Movement on American Pharmacy and Medicine," Ph.D. thesis, (University of Wisconsin, 1954), p. 18.

16. Wooster Beach, *The American Practice of Medicine; Being a Treatise on the Character, Causes, Symptoms, Morbid Appearances and Treatment of the Diseases of Men, Women, and Children . . . As Taught at the Reformed Medical Colleges in the United States: Containing Also a Treatise on Materia Medica and Pharmacy . . . with an Appendix on the Cholera* (3 vols. New York, 1833). Beach drew heavily on C. S. Rafinesque's *Medical Flora* published in 1828 and Elisha Smith's (no relation to Elias) *The Botanic Physician* of 1830.

ing of journals like *The Battle-Axe* and *The Ishmaelite* and cooperating with the Workingmen's Party in New York in its assault on medical licensing.[17] This combination of religious zeal and common opposition to licensing gave Eclectics a sense of unity.

Reformed practice spread quickly throughout upper New York state and especially in the area around Rochester. In 1832 the Genessee Union Botanic Society was formed. In the same year a Reform Medical Society was started at Conesus. Two societies, each named the Reformed Medical Association of Western New York, were organized at Danville and Fredonia. Meanwhile, Samuel Thomson's son Cyrus carried Thomsonianism through western New York as he traveled toward Ohio. Another son, John, settled in Albany where he edited the *Botanic Watchman* and gathered signatures for petitions against licensing. For Samuel Thomson the brisk sale of patent rights was "a balm" for all his sufferings.

Thomsonianism had always been strong in New England, especially in Massachusetts and adjacent parts of Vermont and New Hampshire. William Fonerden, a clergyman and botanic doctor, carried the gospel to the South. A Thomsonian college was chartered in Forsyth, Georgia, under Fonerden's influence in 1839, two years after a medical journal, which frequently reprinted Fonerden's expositions of the system, was established at Charleston. The governor of Mississippi estimated that half the state's population was treated according to Thomsonian principles. Before sweeping through the South, however, Thomsonianism had made its presence felt in Ohio. By the mid-thirties, Thomson claimed, half the population of Ohio adhered to his practice, and orthodox physicians conceded that at least a third did.[18]

A hundred thousand patent rights had been sold by 1840 throughout the nation, and since Thomson had not been able to enforce his monopoly, it is probable that a far greater number actually practiced according to his system.[19] According to Thomsonian estimates (which were not disputed by orthodox physicians), it is probable that three to four million people in the country usually preferred treatment by

17. Wilder, *History of Medicine*, pp. 476–81.

18. Madge E. Pickard and R. Carlyle Buley, *The Midwest Pioneer: His Ills, Cures, and Doctors* (Crawfordsville, Ind., 1945), p. 178.

19. The founding of Thomsonian journals destroyed the element of secrecy that Thomson had nurtured, and negated the value of patent rights.

Thomsonian doctors by 1840.[20] Though Thomsonians probably included Eclectics in estimates of their own strength, there were never many Eclectics outside of New York prior to 1850.

The success of Thomsonianism is paradoxical. Its pathology differed in no significant way from that of Galen. Its therapeutics were no more novel. Ever since the botanical renaissance following Europe's expansion in the sixteenth and seventeenth centuries, regular physicians had taken an active interest in botany. David Hosack, for example, kept a valuable botanical garden in New York, and Benjamin Rush, usually cited as a horrible example of orthodox excess, was advising students in 1789 to study indigenous plants for their curative value. As for lobelia, the Penobscot Indians used it for certain ailments and communicated knowledge of its emetic function to colonial New Englanders. Nor is lobelia's superiority to orthodox emetics clear. Thomson argued that the vomiting it produced was not severe in comparison with the protracted nausea and lasting debility induced by tartar emetic. But, after all, when one vomits, one vomits; it is often difficult to distinguish grades of unpleasantness. In addition to containing little that was new, Eclectic medicine was closer to regular practice than was Thomsonianism. How, then, can the remarkable appeal of botanic medicine in the thirties be accounted for?

THOMSONIANISM AS POLITICAL THEORY

To master Thomson's pathology and therapy seemed to require no considerable wit. While the number of herbs in his materia medica was large, wide choice was allowed within the context of his course of treatment. The system, his followers argued, was "quite too simple to suit the refined taste of the learned Latin and Greeklings of this learned age." It was so simple that, Thomson concluded, a medical profession was superfluous. "To make every man his own physician" became the rallying cry of the movement.[21] The family, not the infirmary, was to be the center of medical advice.

However extravagant his language, there was nothing absurd about Thomson's assumption that domestic practitioners could put the pro-

20. Pickard and Buley, *The Midwest Pioneer*, p. 178.
21. *Boston Thomsonian Manual, 1* (Nov. 1835), 8; *1* (June 1835), 14; *3* (Nov. 15, 1837), 21.

fession to flight. The presence of a medical elite in the larger towns and cities did not end the medical role of people who claimed only a knack for curing disease. One of the most respected medical men in late eighteenth-century Windsor, Connecticut, for example, was a freed Negro called "Dr. Primus." [22] In New Jersey, medical practice, except in extraordinary cases, was mainly in the hands of women as late as 1818, and in one county, Cape May, no educated physician had yet been able to establish himself.[23] Elsewhere the reluctance of sick people to consult formally qualified doctors for routine ailments forced even graduate physicians into a wide variety of pursuits with little or no medical connection. Ashbel Robertson of Wethersfield, Connecticut, for example, took an M.D. degree from Yale in 1815 but was also a licensed wineseller and maintained a mercantile business until 1834.[24] The multiplication of medical schools in the early nineteenth century began to provide a stream of graduates formally qualified if actually only semicompetent, to undercut domestic practitioners. But there were still many of the latter in the thirties. Thomson equipped these people with a readily comprehensible scientific glossary and added a public image for his movement that was to touch strings peculiarly sensitive in the thirties.

Thomsonians viewed themselves in alternating perspectives. At times they saw their movement as wresting medicine from the doctors and completing the great revolution which, beginning with the Reformation, freed government from the lawyers and despots and religion from the priests; at other times as intimately involved in a mighty reformation in which there was still much to be done to secure to the common man his rights in government as well as medicine.[25] In their latter role Thomsonians throughout the thirties

22. Henry R. Stiles, *The History of Ancient Windsor, Connecticut* (2 vols. New York, 1859, 1892), *1*, 879–80.

23. David B. Warden, *A Statistical, Political, and Historical Account of the United States of North America: From the Period of Their First Colonization to the Present Day* (3 vols. Edinburgh, 1819), *2*, 50.

24. Henry R. Stiles, *The History of Ancient Wethersfield, Connecticut* (2 vols. New York, 1904), *2*, 585. See also C. Bancroft Gillespie, *An Historic Record and Pictorical Description of the Town of Meriden, Connecticut, and Men Who Made It* (Meriden, 1906), pp. 239–40; William F. Seward, ed., *Binghampton and Broome County, New York: A History* (3 vols. New York, 1924), *1*, 220.

25. Samuel Thomson, *Introduction to the New Guide to Health* (4th ed. Columbus, 1827), pp. 2–3.

attached themselves to a wide range of political and social reforms.

Their opponents were invariably branded as an aristocracy propped up by servile minions and pensioned presses. While the common man was said to prefer steam baths and lobelia, the nobility could think only of calomel and the lancet, and to gratify its lurid tastes had created a privileged order of physicians "that make the rich,—richer, the poor,—poorer." [26]

Not the moderately prosperous but the "idle rich" were the targets of Thomsonian abuse. But who were the idle rich? Few fortunes came from inheritance in the thirties and even fewer were made by dawdlers. The answer lay in the oft-sounded theme of manual labor. There was not a more truly valuable class of persons, a Thomsonian journal asserted, than the mechanics:

> They are . . . the producers of wealth; their labor gives to us the necessaries and luxuries of life; while their practical intelligence and the stern virtues in which they are schooled, give stability and safety to our free institutions.[27]

In contrast to the idle rich, it added, the mechanics did not rack their brains "in driving some gambling speculation by which they hope to amass sudden wealth." Leon Brunschvicg has called the search for the parasite—the odd man out in the production of wealth —the "darling vice" of nineteenth-century political theory. Radical Jacksonians were intent upon this search and climaxed it with discovery of the parasitical nature of "fictitious" wealth, wealth based on stocks and paper money. In their denunciation of the nonproducer, Thomsonians were only echoing the popular ideology that had forced even Daniel Webster to reassess the merit of the moneyed aristocrat by 1840.

Along with glorification of manual labor went an assertion of the special value of useful knowledge. The *North American Review,* not normally disposed to radical pronouncements, warned in 1833 that only knowledge applied to use could fulfill the designs of an enlightened freedom.[28] Not long afterward George Ripley, a prominent Boston minister and member of the Transcendental Club, took the

26. *Thomsonian Botanic Watchman, 1* (Oct. 1834) , 148.
27. *Boston Thomsonian Manual, 7* (March 15, 1841) , 135.
28. "Popular Education," *North American Review, 36* (Jan. 1833) , 73.

lead in establishing at West Roxbury the Brook Farm community in order to combine intellectual speculation with labor in the fields. Thomsonians, themselves arrayed against the sons of "mystery loving Paracelsus," went further, asserting that productive labor derives little or no advantage from academies and colleges:

> Few of the youth who enter their halls, ever seek for a livelihood in the laboring arts. They learn to look upon labor as servile and demeaning, and seek their living in what they consider the higher classes of society. They are virtually withdrawn from the producing classes.

In addition, mechanics were doomed to subservience to "nonproducing thinkers" unless they formed their own lyceums and libraries, just as all citizens would be shackled by the "learned quackery" of orthodox medicine until they mastered the useful botanic precepts for self-medication.[29]

On a more personal level Thomsonians sought to identify their cause with Andrew Jackson. Thomson himself was an avid supporter of Jackson, and the credulous were attracted by his assertion that, since Jackson's administration had granted him a patent, the President personally approved his system. To Daniel Drake this was simply another instance of an unbalanced public's intoxication with slogans:

> Oh! to take medicine "by authority" and that, too, of the President, who would recommend nothing that he had not tried on himself, and found useful for the people. He is the people's friend. He is a good doctor (not from book-larnin') but from common sense; he once made a great speech in Congress, and that shows he is a great *doctor!* before that he was a great *lawyer,* and of course is a great *doctor!* he fought a great *battle,* and is therefore a great *doctor.*[30]

In Jackson, popular orators found the embodiment of democratic virtue; native ability over artifice, simplicity over ostentation, inde-

29. *Boston Thomsonian Manual,* 7 (June 1, 1841), 215.
30. Daniel Drake, "The People's Doctors," *West. J. Med. Phys. Sciences,* 3 (Oct.-Dec. 1829), 407.

pendence over servility. It was to Thomson's credit as a publicist that he was able to turn the image of a man who preferred calomel and bloodletting on his deathbed to the purposes of a radical medical sect which disdained both.

The concomitant of identification with the people was opposition to special privilege in the form of licensed monopoly. "The benefit of even limited monopolies," Jefferson wrote, "is too doubtful to be opposed to that of their general suppression." [31] To Jeffersonians monopolies fostered stock-jobbery and, inevitably, fictitious aristocracy. Agitation against monopolies, never wholly moribund, was revived in New York in the late twenties by opponents of Van Buren's policy of dispensing patronage by the selective granting of charters and fanned by the contemporary outcry against Masonry. The Democrats, noting the popularity of antimonopoly slogans, successfully turned them against the Whigs' "monster bank" in Philadelphia. Thomsonians, with their own ax to grind on licensing legislation, naturally joined in the assault on all forms of licensed monopoly. In practice, this took the form of cooperation with the Workingmen's Party. Botanic doctors, Thomsonian and Eclectic, attended public meetings of mechanics opposed to paper money and banking and to all licensed monopolies. Job Haskell, the Workingmen's leader, was the principal spokesman for Thomsonians in the New York assembly. Thomsonians were, he declared, "slaves to those privileged doctors" and, like himself, assailed "by the artillery of a privileged order." The continued reluctance of the assembly to repeal the laws was ascribed to the "total want of *consistency, honesty,* and *republicanism*" on the part of "self-styled republicans." [32]

The antimonopoly theme readily admitted local variations. In South Carolina, where egalitarian agitation had quieted after an alliance of Charleston and up-country radicals had gained reapportionment in 1808 and manhood suffrage in 1810, Thomsonians talked more of free trade in medicine, as in commerce, and drew up addresses to the Free Trade and States Rights party calling for repeal of the "medical tariff." But this line of attack was combined

31. Jefferson to Madison, July 31, 1788, in Julian P. Boyd, ed., *The Papers of Thomas Jefferson* (Princeton, 1956), *13*, 443.
32. *Man* (New York City), May 15, 1834; April 30, 1835; April 27, 1835.

with the general theme that defenders of licensing were aristocrats, descendants of the "most royal race of Tories." [33]

Lending plausibility to the Thomsonian depiction of their struggle as one between democracy and aristocracy were conservative and cliquish proclivities fashionable at the top of the profession. In South Carolina Samuel Dickson, F. Y. Porcher, and both Moultries had been Unionists in 1833 and later, with J. P. Jervey, John Bellinger, and Governor Thomas Bennett (a defender of medical licensing), they formed an active Clay Club. The Unionist, Benjamin Perry, described repeal as "a Loco Foco retrograde." [34] In New York and Massachusetts in an earlier day Samuel Latham Mitchill and Benjamin Waterhouse were looked on as mavericks by the profession's elite for their Jeffersonian sentiments.

Clannishness had done little to enhance the public image of the profession. At a time of popular agitation against Masonry, orthodox physicians were unfortunate to have in their midst an even more exclusive fraternity, Kappa Lambda. Founded in 1820 by Samuel Brown, an imaginative medical professor at Transylvania University, Kappa Lambda flourished principally in Lexington, Philadelphia, and New York. Brown had envisioned a great national fraternity to promote fellowship and advance science. The former object was readily admitted by the New York County society:

> and the means used for securing it, . . . lauded for ingenuity and aptness. Indeed, never has the physiological fact of a close sympathy between the heart and stomach, been more experimentally proved.[35]

Within the profession, however, Kappa Lambda was a source of disharmony. Brown's idea was anachronistic even in 1820; a private club could add little to a profession already legally organized.

Secrecy and exclusiveness were allegedly the hallmarks of the fraternity in New York. Concerning secrecy there can be some question.

33. *So. Bot. J., 1* (Aug. 19, 1837); 2 (Dec. 22, 1838), 338; Daniel F. Nardin, *An Address to the People of South Carolina Shewing the Unconstitutionality, Injustice and Impolicy of the Medical Law of the State* (Charleston, 1835), p. 30 and passim.

34. *So. Bot. J., 2* (Dec. 22, 1838), 345.

35. *Report of the Committee of the Medical Society of the City and County of New York appointed to investigate the subject of a Secret Medical Association* (New York, 1831), p. 3.

For a clandestine organization Kappa Lambda's activities and membership were well known. Exclusive, however, it certainly was. Candidates had to be unanimously approved on two successive ballots. This naturally bred jealously among the "outs," and compounding resentment were two additional factors. The fraternity was, first of all, enmeshed in medical politics in the city. Most of the trustees of the College of Physicians and Surgeons prior to 1826, including John R. Manley, John Augustine Smith, Alexander H. Stevens, Edward Delafield, and F. U. Johnstone, were members. After disposing of Hosack and his colleagues they appointed themselves to the lucrative professorships. When excluded members of the county society began to glance fondly in the direction of the faculty chairs and found them occupied by members of Kappa Lambda, they attributed their frustration to the fraternity. Further, Kappa Lambda was charged with monopolizing the major hospital posts that led to practice and conferred reputation. At the New York Hospital six of the seven attending physicians and surgeons belonged to the fraternity as did all the consultants at the City Dispensary.

One need not accept all criticisms of Kappa Lambda at face value. Its members were among the most distinguished physicians of the city, men who would have occupied the key posts in any event.[36] But of greater significance is the fact that the fraternity's only real function, self-perpetuation, was incompatible with the harmony and good reputation of the profession. The bubble burst in 1838 when the *New York Whig* published an exposé of Kappa Lambda's machinations during a county society election.[37] "Secret, dark, impalpable," its existence, "like that of the blighting miasm," could be known only by its effects. This was nonsense, but popular nonsense with a telling effect. The *Whig* (Feb. 8, 1839) reported:

36. Of the six fraternity physicians at the New York Hospital, four had been appointed before Kappa Lambda's foundation. The City Dispensary naturally drew its consultants from the staff of the New York Hospital, the only real hospital in the city. But attendants could pick their successors and would be well disposed toward fraternity brothers. The most prominent figures of the twenties could thus determine who was to be most prominent in the following decade. See also Philip Van Ingen, "Remarks on 'Kappa Lambda, Elf or Ogre' and a little more concerning the Society," *Bull. Hist. Med.*, *18* (Dec. 1945), 513–38.

37. *A History of the New York Kappa Lambda Conspiracy* (New York, 1839), p. 3. The *History* was based on articles published in the *Whig* in 1838.

> The members are dispersing themselves; they have lost
> their unity of action, and are making love to all parties—
> are pretending a great interest in those whom, up to the
> publication of our articles, they invariably attempted to
> crush.

Though Kappa Lambda survived in New York until 1862, its power
had been broken. A libel suit brought by George McClellan, the
founder of Jefferson Medical College, against a fraternity member in
Philadelphia in 1828 hastened the demise of Kappa Lambda in that
city and damaged the reputation of the profession as a whole.

Few pitfalls are more dangerous for historians than confusion of
rhetoric and reality. Nothing would have surprised the average licensed physician more than to find himself included in the aristocracy of wealth. Outside of the select circles in which Hosack, the
Warrens, Dickson, and other leaders of the profession moved, there
is little evidence of a general connection between social position and
the type of physician employed.

Though Thomsonians claimed that they were doctors of the common people, they were in no worse financial position than orthodox
physicians. Even before Thomsonianism had begun to decline, the
friendly botanic societies were dwindling in importance. Some members were found more suited than others for medicine and were
deputed to practice generally. Although these Thomsonian practitioners often held other forms of employment at the same time, there
is no reason to suppose that their fees were generally lower than those
of regular physicians. Botanics could not sue for payments, but they
usually contracted for a set fee in advance. This was, in fact, the same
system used throughout the country by most licensed doctors.
Though the latter experimented with fee tables, they had little success. The table established by New York physicians in 1790, for example, had to be reprinted in 1825 "in consequence of the inattention and even ignorance so prevalent upon the subject of fees." [38]
Where attempts were made to enforce the tables, as in South Carolina, professional acrimony was the result.

Many orthodox physicians, in addition to contracting in advance,

38. Quoted in George Rosen, *Fees and Fee Bills: Some Economic Aspects of Medical
Practice in Nineteenth Century America* (reprinted from Supplement 6 to the Bulletin
of the History of Medicine, 1946), p. 2.

had to extend credit on a yearly basis. In some rural areas of New England the practice was to allow fees to accumulate indefinitely until they were finally paid in kind. Boston physicians also relied on the credit system, though it meant "loosing [sic] half, and often the whole." [39] The same system prevailed in Mississippi with the result that "from one fourth to one third of our annual charges are never realized." [40] Though a "generous, liberal, disinterested class," physicians by no means formed part of the "monied aristocracy." [41]

If Thomsonians distorted the picture in branding regular physicians lackeys of the plutocracy, they succeeded, nevertheless, in stirring up suspicion of their opponents' motives in seeking a privileged legal position and elicited from regular physicians profuse declarations of disinterestedness. This suspicion, however, was more strongly rooted in the country at large than within legislative chambers.

Not only did Whigs and Democrats advocate or oppose repeal in similar proportions in New York,[42] but some Loco-Foco Democrats remained unmoved by the antimonopoly rhetoric of Thomson's followers. One of the bitterest foes of Thomsonians, for example, was Michael Hoffmann, a comrade of Van Buren, Governor Silas Wright, and all the major New York Jacksonians. The explanation lies in the fact that by 1844 most politicians were coming to regard antimonopoly rhetoric as a substitute for thought. While paying due obeisance on the campaign trail, they saw it as less and less germane to affairs of state.

Nothing could have been more irrelevant, in one respect, than Thomsonian rhetoric in South Carolina. The States Rights and Free Trade party to which Thomsonians were speaking in 1838 had ceased to exist with the settlement of the Nullification Crisis five years previously. Practically no one in South Carolina was against free trade. Not that, but the scope of states rights in a federal republic,

39. *Boston Med. Surg. J.*, *46* (May 26, 1852) , 345.

40. Quoted in Rosen, *Fees and Fee Bills*, p. 17.

41. "The Pecuniary Condition of the Medical Profession in the United States," *Boston Med. Surg. J.*, *4* (Feb. 15, 1831) , 10. One may place more credence in the observation of regular physicians, invariably made in chagrin, that Thomsonians often were patronized by the more respectable members of the community; see Drake, "The People's Doctors," p. 407.

42. Democrats, 56.1 per cent (41 of 73 voting) , and 71.7 per cent of the Whigs (20 of 28 voting) favored repeal; *N.Y. J. Ass.*, 67 sess. (1844) , p. 1042; *Albany Argus*, Nov. 14, 1843, for party affiliation.

had been at issue in 1833. Practically no one was against states rights; the Unionists had called themselves the "Union and States Rights Party." In 1838 two proposals were put before the legislature: removal of the fines and prohibition on fee collection of the 1817 law, and an amendment by William F. Colcock to repeal only the fines. Colcock was the son of Judge Charles Colcock and, like his father, a strict states rights man. Some former Unionists, like Benjamin F. Perry, opposed any form of repeal; others, such as C. G. Memminger and Daniel Huger, voted for Colcock's amendment. But most legislators had not played a significant role on either side in 1833. Thomsonians hardly seem to have formed an alliance of all former nullifiers against licensing.

In another respect, however, Thomsonian rhetoric was highly relevant. By appealing to no one they appealed, in effect, to everyone. There was no real opposition to antimonopoly oratory in New York or to free trade oratory in South Carolina. The South Carolina legislator who claimed that he voted against licensing in the name of "Free Trade and Sailors' Rights" spoke for popular feeling. If Thomsonian slogans bore little relation to actuality, they were, nonetheless, highly potent as oratory. The one argument for repeal that even orthodox physicians could not dispute was that licensing was unenforceable, that it "has not prevented, nor can it prevent the spread of the Thomsonian system." [43] The popularity of botanic doctors, which frustrated every attempt at enforcement, owed much to their use of these slogans. While this had little effect on leading political figures, it was decisive among the less sophisticated.

The success of Thomsonians was due in part to their near monopoly among medical practitioners of popular rhetoric, and to their generally sincere identification with radical causes. Many orthodox physicians doubtless were equally interested in social improvement, but this concern was expressed only by individuals, never through the profession itself. As a consequence, orthodoxy seemed closer to reform's baggage train than its van.

Thomsonianism As Cultural Expression

Thomsonian zeal, however, was too fervid to be exhausted in political channels. If its success was partly due to its timely identifica-

43. *So. Bot. J.*, 2 (Dec. 22, 1838), 345; *1* (April 1, 1837), 75.

tion with popular political causes, its sensitivity to social and intellectual currents of the thirties was no less important.

Because bodily processes such as menstruation and pregnancy influence a considerable part of women's lives and because women are principally entrusted with the health of children, lay women tend today, and tended formerly, to be more interested in medicine than lay men, and more susceptible to the lure of medical sects and panaceas. An orthodox physician wrote,

> Everyone knows that no young physician can succeed without the approbation of the maids and matrons of his particular precinct. He is held amenable to their tribunal;— their approving smiles give him life, and hope, and prosperity; or their disapprobation, like the frowns of some angry deity, drives him to despair. He may pass the most rigid examination at Boston, New York, Philadelphia or London, yet if he cannot gain the approbation of this last board, every other testimonial must pass for nothing.[44]

That female influence in medical matters had often promoted empiricism was frequently observed. Women were repelled by the barbarity and uncertainty of heroic practice and sought refuge in catholic remedies. Little wonder that a correspondent of the *Boston Medical and Surgical Journal* attributed the success of quackery in ninety-nine cases out of a hundred to the ladies.[45]

"To the female portion of the community in an especial manner," the Thomsonians made their appeal:[46]

> Upon them have the evils of the poisoning and "forcing" practice fallen with fearfully redoubled weight, and it has been through their shattered and broken constitutions that mankind have most sorely suffered from the effects of learned quackery.

With Thomsonianism "dawned a new era for afflicted woman; and the strength of her faith and testimony, after having once become ac-

44. Dan King, *Quackery Unmasked* (New York, ca. 1858), pp. 261–62.
45. "Lady Abettors of Quackery," *36* (March 10, 1847), 128.
46. *Boston Thomsonian Manual*, preface to vols. 1 and 2 (Boston, 1835–37), iv.

quainted with its effects and merits, conclusively shows the value which she places on it." Though Thomsonians made free use of purgatives, they depicted calomel as a "skin-defacer—beauty's foe." More important, the one feature of orthodox practice never adopted by Thomsonianism was bleeding. The usual technique in phlebotomy was application of leeches to the neck, thus leaving permanent marks. Whatever the attitude of eighteenth-century women, few fashion-conscious females in an age of relatively daring necklines like the thirties were likely to favor it.

The relationship between women and Thomsonianism, however, went farther than the latter's appeal to distaff vanity. Led by William Smellie of Edinburgh, male practitioners had brought improved instruments and a less empirical approach to midwifery during the eighteenth century and thus sharply reduced the importance of female midwives. By 1800 the most common type of practitioner in England was the surgeon–apothecary–man midwife. The growing popularity of exotic mineral remedies, generally available only to male apothecaries, was an additional factor in the supplanting of the village women of earlier ages by men. In America similar developments took place more slowly because of the rougher nature of society but were coming to prominence in the thirties. This trend was spurred by the contemporary sentimentalization of personal relationships and the fashionable image of women as pallid and delicate adornments of society, unfit for the rigors of medical practice.

Exclusion from the learned professions (except teaching) was not the only inequity confronting women. From a legal viewpoint they were considered perpetual minors; if married, a part of their husbands' chattels; if single, the ward of male relatives. Wife-beating "with a reasonable instrument" was lawful in almost every state as late as 1850. Organized protests against their condition began after 1830 with women's rights societies. For the first time women showed a vital concern with political issues. Whether making up the rank and file of the peace and abolition crusades or publicizing the temperance cause, their activities attracted attention and often consternation.

Conceptulizations of the proper role of women in society abound in the pages of *Godey's Lady's Book*. The problem was defined (March 1842, p. 190) by L. G. Tasistro:

Women and the working classes are, as regards cultivation, similarly circumstanced. Few now dispute their right to knowledge; but the best mode of presenting them with it, and the best mode of rendering the gift beneficial, remains yet an unsolved problem.

With man's only claim to superiority—"the rule of might as opposed to right"—having been exploded by the modern refinement of taste, some found it the intent of nature that women should now predominate. But Tasistro's theme emphasized her role of providing beauty in daily life as opposed to self-aggrandizement. Women's simple art of "not too much" would restrain even the ambitious of her sex from excess.

The happiest aspect of Thomsonianism, as far as its appeal to women was concerned, was that it opened medical practice to them without forcing a confrontation of the sensitive question of whether a woman should ever treat a man other than her husband. Samuel Thomson had replaced the infirmary with the family, and particularly the mother of the family. While male patent holders frequently practiced outside the friendly botanic societies, women could confine their efforts to immediate relatives and were thus saved the inevitable blushes consequent upon having to treat strangers. Obeisances were paid to sentimentality as well as to feminism.

Thomsonians considered themselves in the fore of the feminist movement. Since the founder had said nearly all there was to say about medicine, their journals devoted themselves mainly to publicizing his ideas. In contrast to the academic tone of orthodox medical periodicals, botanic journals were directed to the laity and printed numerous articles extolling women and their expanded role in society. Special attention was given to the importance of trained female midwives. John Thomson wrote:

> We cannot deny that women possess superior capacities for the science of medicine, and although men should reserve to themselves the exclusive right to mend broken limbs and fractured skulls, and to prescribe in all cases for their own sex, they should certainly give up to women the office of attending upon women.[47]

47. *Thomsonian Botanic Watchman, 1* (Dec. 1, 1834), 182.

119

In reopening midwifery to females and in giving them a distinct medical role in their own families, Thomsonians thus reconciled the conflicting notions about women common in the thirties.

Evidence about the extent of female involvement in the botanic crusade before 1840 is necessarily indirect. Women's names were rarely brought before the public, nor were women elected to executive positions in the movement. That they attended meetings of friendly botanic societies is evident from the form of address—"ladies and gentlemen"—used by some Thomsonian speakers. Significantly, women never attended orthodox medical conventions. After 1840 Thomsonianism grew more institutionalized and was supplanted by neo-Thomsonianism and Eclecticism. For the historian the botanic movement becomes, if less interesting, easier to follow.

The graduation of Elizabeth Blackwell from Geneva Medical College in upstate New York in 1849 has engaged considerable attention. But a more important event in the history of women's entrance into the profession occurred in the same year when the Eclectic Central Medical College at Syracuse commenced a policy of co-education. Miss Blackwell's medical degree was an episode, not part of a policy. Geneva College passed a resolution to enroll no more female students until after her graduation and did not actually admit another woman before 1860. Most regular doctors were prostrated at the thought of "Madam in *boots* and *bloomer*" approaching the profession. Not that they were misogynists. Woman, they affirmed, was "the pride and glory of the race—the sacred repository of all that is virtuous, graceful and lovely." [48] But in seeking to practice medicine Elizabeth Blackwell had strayed from her proper element. It would have been in perfect keeping with their transactions if a "clique of pseudo-reformers, or some mushroom Thomsonian or hydropathic association, had conferred the degree." [49] But orthodox physic did not have to continue this anomaly. The task of further medical education for women fell to Eclectics.

In 1847 Harriet Kezia Hunt, an unlicensed physician, was denied admission to Harvard Medical School because of her sex. At that time Samuel Gregory was lecturing in Boston on various aspects of

48. P. W. Leland, "Empiricism and Its Causes," *Boston Med. Surg. J.*, 47 (Nov. 3, 1849) , 58.

49. *Boston Med. Surg. J.*, 47 (Feb. 21, 1849) , 58, 59.

mesmerism and concerning himself with the cause of female medical education. Born in 1813 in Guilford, Vermont, Gregory did not enter Yale until he was twenty-three. He took his Bachelor's degree in 1840 and Master's five years later. Finally, his interest in medicine led him to the Penn Medical College, an Eclectic school (no relation to any present institution) in Philadelphia. Before graduation, however, he had played the major role in establishing the first female medical college in New England.[50]

Denouncing the practice of obstetrics by men, Gregory declared that in no other country were women so dependent "upon the opposite sex for assistance on these occasions as in our own." His argument was, typically, a combination of sentiment and reason. The more the physician is esteemed as a friend and acquaintance,

> so much the more it increases and complicates the embarrassment. Hence many an estimable female, seeking relief from her distress, passes by the learned and respected physician, and commits herself to some unprincipled quack, *because* she neither regards him nor values his regard for her.[51]

To provide instruction in his college Gregory secured the services of two regular physicians, William Mason Cornell and Enoch Carter Rolfe. But the majority of orthodox doctors assailed the new college, and its closest ties were with the irregular Female Medical College in Philadelphia.[52] An invitation to regular physicians to join the latter faculty had been summarily rejected. As a consequence the professors were drawn mainly from physicians who had abandoned regular medicine to join one of the medical sectarian organizations. The Boston and Philadelphia colleges were merged in 1852, the faculty

50. Frederick C. Waite, *History of the New England Female Medical College, 1848–1874* (Boston, 1950), pp. 11–13.

51. Samuel Gregory, *Letters to Ladies in favor of Female Physicians for Their Own Sex* (Boston, 1856), pp. 9, 12. The suspicious read even more sinister motives into male midwifery. A Methodist preacher turned Thomsonian doctor charged that any woman so profligate as to let a man deliver her child "would let that same Doctor afterwards get her with child, if he chose to do so"; quoted in Young, *Toadstool Millionaires*, p. 53.

52. Waite, *History of New England Female Medical College*, p. 27, passim; a recent account of the New England College can be found in John B. Blake, "Women and Medicine in Ante-Bellum America," *Bull. Hist. Med.*, 39 (March–April 1965), 115, 118.

chiefly Eclectic but including Rolfe and Cornell. After that date regular physicians consented to join the Philadelphia faculty and Eclectics left both colleges. The New England Female Medical College could grant a certificate in midwifery, not an M.D. degree. Graduates who did not wish to confine themselves to midwifery and nursing could obtain the medical degree from the coeducational Eclectic college in Syracuse.

Samuel Gregory spoke of "delicacy and morality" where Samuel Thomson had discoursed on "well-my-gristle" and "ramcats." Eclecticism, with its refinement, and dilution, was more akin to homoeopathy than to the rough creed of Thomson. But Eclecticism and Thomsonianism were at one in opening medical practice to women.

A prejudice against the use of surgical instruments in childbirth prevaded Gregory's writings on midwifery. Only when nature was "shocked and paralyzed" by the presence of a male did the work have to be accomplished "by the poor substitute of art." [53] Attendance by females would calm the expectant mother and banish the need for forceps and like instruments. In thus emphasizing nature over art Gregory was repeating a doctrine long cherished by Thomsonians.

The simplest form of the Thomsonian defense of nature was an assertion that certain people had a special gift for healing; those lacking this knack could never be successful, regardless of their academic learning. From this belief they derived a hostility to the ostentatious verbiage and allegedly meaningless taxonomy of orthodox medical colleges.

Never ones to go halfway, Thomsonians combined the nature theme with an affirmation of nationalism and divine providence. Samuel Thomson had argued that domestic herbs were more suited to American constitutions.[54] In the same spirit the masthead of the *Thomsonian Botanic Watchman* depicted "the sun of science rising over the flora of North America." A body of Thomsonian petitioners from upstate New York noted the "salutary effects upon the Humane

53. Gregory, *Letters to Ladies*, p. 32.

54. Samuel Thomson, *Narrative and Introduction to the New Guide to Health* (Columbus, 1827), p. 162. The doctrine that the plants of a region were best suited to inhabitants of the region had a long history in folk medicine. Thomsonians gave the doctrine a distinctly national, not regional, orientation.

System of the medicines growing Spontaneously in our Country."
These, they declared, "far exceed Chemical preparations or imported
medicines." To the God of Nature man owed the endowment of
"each plant and flower with medical power." [55]

Though separable in logic, the themes of nature, providence,
and nationalism were usually expressed concomitantly. Speaking on
behalf of the Thomsonians, a New York state senator maintained in
1844:

> The study of the healing art may be pursued to as great
> advantage by the inquiring and enlightened mind, by read-
> ing the great book of nature, which a wise and bountiful
> providence has spread before him; and obtain from it as
> great a knowledge of the healing qualities of the roots of
> plants, flowers and leaves, which God has designed for the
> healing on the people, as can be obtained from the study of
> musty books in the halls of institutions of materia media. [56]

Thomsonians were by no means the sole beneficiaries of the popular romantic cult of nature. Nearly every town had its "natural"
bonesetter who claimed that his success rested on genius, not study.
Perhaps the most famous of these practitioners, the Sweet family of
Rhode Island, had for three generations plied their craft throughout
the East. Even more common were the "Indian doctors," at times
aboriginals but usually mulattoes. These traveling charlatans (one
had to deny that his office was the Mexican Gulf Railroad) marketed
a wide range of native vegetable medicaments. An advertisement for
the "Indian Panacea" ridiculed the pretensions of orthodox physicians who practiced by means of art alone and overlooked:

> the rich and bounteous stores of medicines, which the Al-
> mighty has caused to spring out of the earth in every clime!
> And how much more time it is, that while the American
> physician looks to foreign countries for many of his most
> common necessary articles, perpetually changing as they
> are, at the dictates of fashion or folly, he is surrounded in

55. "Report of the committee on medical societies . . . ," *N.Y. Docs. of Ass.* (1834) , 2,
no. 95.

56. "Remarks of Mr. Scott in the senate . . . ," *Trans., Med. Soc. State N.Y.,* 6
(1844–46) , appendix for 1844, 73.

his own country with an endless profusion of medical plants, sufficient to answer any indication in disease or to answer any curable disorder.[57]

Though most mineral remedies were dismissed as "unnatural," one short-lived sectarian organization, the Massachusetts Physo-Medical Society, resolved in 1850 to expel members who used even vegetable remedies which did not act "in unison with the laws of nature.[58] When the leading Thomsonian editor, D. F. Nardin, told a meeting at the Barnwell, South Carolina, courthouse that the true reformer of medicine would have to be "a child of nature, who was not spoiled by art," he was simply echoing one aspect of the popular prejudice against human contrivances in treating disease.[59]

In their cruder moments Thomsonians conceived of nature as a collection of herbs whose remedial efficacy was guaranteed by divine intervention. A more refined interpretation was possible. Behind the wondrous flora of North America, and, indeed, behind all medical science were natural laws, defiance of which was always attended by sickness. Confidence in natural laws harmonized with the dominant theological moods of optimism and perfectionism and brought sectarian medicine into association with the liberal clergy. A. P. Peabody, Plummer Professor at Harvard, had insisted in 1842 that Newton could never have discovered the law of gravitation had he been a polytheist. "He inferred, as had preceding *Christian* philosophers, from unity of God the unity of creation." [60] Not merely was the universe marvelous for the simplicity of its laws, but the laws themselves were as beneficent as their Creator. Disease was not a punishment for our "general sins,—our Sabbath-breaking, our pride, our irreligion" but was due to "our special violation of those laws of God established for our physical well being"; sin, once the cause of all sickness, became merely a convenient explanation for certain diseases —"the seeds of consumption, scrofula, insanity, and imperfect constitutions"—that were clearly not attributable to inattention to diet and regimen.[61] For the most part, however, God's wrath was visited upon the glutton, not the infidel.

57. *Charleston Mercury*, Oct. 13, 1838.
58. *Boston Med. Surg. J., 43* (Sept. 4, 1850), 103.
59. *So. Bot. J., 1* (Oct. 24, 1837), 295.
60. [A.P. Peabody], "The Bible," *Christian Examiner*, 3 ser., *15* (Nov. 1842), 154.
61. [Edward Jarvis], "Law of Physical Life," ibid., 3 ser., *17* (Sept. 1843), 28, 31.

An orthodox *Journal of Health* had existed briefly in Philadelphia in the early thirties, and Jacob Bigelow delivered his famous lecture "On Self-limited Diseases" in 1835, but, though few orthodox doctors would have disputed Thoreau's measurement of health by sympathy with morning and spring, they generally showed an understandable reluctance until well after 1840 to commit their patients to nature's curative force.[62]

In this there was much paradox. Thomson himself was no mean doser and held out little hope for patients unwilling to submit to his course. But from the start lobelia had been presented as a milder purgative than "hydra-headed" calomel. Thomsonian journals were devoting considerable attention to the *vis medicatrix naturae* at a time when orthodox physicians were only beginning to grow suspicious of heroic treatment.

The least controversial aspect of Thomsonian enthusiasm for diet and regimen was condemnation of alcohol and tobacco. These denunciations were often rendered in absurd terms; tobacco was said to produce a sinking sensation at the pit of the stomach. However fanciful, they usually took up about as much space in Thomsonian journals as expositions of the system.

Characteristically, Thomsonian energies could not be restrained by conventional boundaries. If the step from an appreciation of the importance of diet and regimine to endorsement of health fads was not a logical one, it was one which many Thomsonians could not resist.

Sylvester Graham, the inventor of "Graham bread" and "Graham crackers," was drawn by his commitment to the Presbyterian ministry to an espousal of the temperance cause.[63] But his fertile mind was soon in search of a more novel solution for mankind's ills, and he found it in vegetarianism. Graham's lectures drew large audiences in the thirities and, shortly before 1840, Alva Curtis, who on Thomson's death in 1843 became the most important figure in the botanic movement, was converted to Grahamism. In the pages of his journal, the *Botanico-Medical Recorder* of Cincinnati, he trumpeted Graham's ideas throughout the Thomsonian world and, for good measure, added mesmerism and phrenology. The last two causes, Curtis

62. Orthodox journals, in addition, printed few articles on diet and regimen, and denounced health fads like Grahamism.

63. M. V. Naylor, "Sylvester Graham, 1794–1851," *Ann. Med. Hist.* 3 ser., *4* (May 1942), 236.

asserted, had been taken up long before 1845 by Thomsonians in Cincinnati, despite derision by orthodox physicians. Many correspondents of the *Recorder* also affirmed themselves believers in Grahamism and phrenology, but the cause of frugality in diet attracted greatest enthusiasm. One Thomsonian wrote,

> Twenty years have now elapsed since we openly proclaimed against the use of alcohol, tobacco, tea, coffee, etc. We have nine children, the oldest one twenty years of age and I do not recollect that I ever saw one of them drink a cup of tea or coffee.[64]

All Thomsonian journals advocated temperance, but most were reluctant to go as far as Curtis. The "numerous and glaring absurdities" of Grahamism were underscored by the *Southern Botanic Journal*, (May 15, 1839), and one correspondent accused Curtis of sacrificing steam and lobelia "at the shrine of *bran bread* and *saw dust* pudding." In the latter charge there was a larger truth. The significance of Curtis' attachment to Grahamism lies in its manifesting the perfectionist concern for reform of all aspects of life, a concern shared by Grahamites and Thomsonians. In 1838 the Grahamite American Health Convention assembled in Boston and resolved:

> That the blessed cause of human improvement, the spread of the Gospel, and the universal regeneration of the world, can never be successfully carried forward without the aid of the great work which we are now assembled to advance.[65]

In a similar vein Thomsonians desired "reform in medicine, dietetics and morals, or, in short, a reform in physiology and morality." [66]

Liberal clergymen found support for their optimistic view of nature in the devotion of Thomsonians and other sects to diet and regimen. The clergy, a physician wrote,

> are often known to make the most strenuous exertions to overthrow what they choose to call the *old* school of medicine, and sometimes whole communities are seen to follow

64. *Bot.-Med. Rec.*, *13* (Feb. 1, 1845), 99; *13* (Jan. 4, 1845), 56; *12* (Sept. 21, 1844), 356–57.
65. *North American Review*, 47 (Oct. 1838), 383.
66. *Bot.-Med. Rec.*, *12* (Sept. 21, 1844), 356–57.

the *ipse dixit* of such a leader, and go over almost *en masse* to some absurd humbug, of the true nature of which they really know nothing.

Such men, he added, "appear to think that a complete revolution is soon to take place in medical matters, and they expect to lead the van to victory." [67]

Clergymen were caught between the decline of their function as medical advisors for their flocks and the rise of perfectionist enthusiasm which called on them to effect the physical as well as spiritual uplifting of their parishioners. Every medical discovery that diminished suffering was seen not merely as a temporal blessing but as a help to the moral and spiritual elevation of the race. Ministers, the *Boston Medical and Surgical Journal* commented, had been taught "a smattering of the *ologies*" in college and then presumed "that they can make a short cut, 'a royal road,' to what proves so long, so arduous, so uncertain a goal, as the educated physician acknowledges his ultimatum to be, after life-long struggles and honest devotion to the truth." [68] Clergymen were asking for more than orthodox physicians could provide and found in the bold pretensions of patented panaceas and sectarian medicine the solution to their problem.

From this meliorist and perfectionist frame of mind sectarian systems and nostrum-mongers alike benefited. The appearance of "the venerable title of Rev." on advertisements for nostrums chagrined regular doctors, especially when they had to behold at the same time "the minister of the Most High, trumpeting forth the praises of Thomsonism, Hahnemannism, hydropathy, and the like." [69] Both Oliver Wendell Holmes and Worthington Hooker noted that some of the chief supporters of homoeopathy, and like delusions were clergymen. [70] Orthodox physicians in Massachusetts

---

67. King, *Quackery Unmasked*, pp. 274–75.

68. "Relations between the Clerical and Medical Professions: The Christian Examiner and the Hydropathic Delusion," *Boston Med. Surg. J.*, *38* (July 26, 1848), 518.

69. J. F. Skinner, "Domestic Medicines," ibid., *40* (May 23, 1849), 313; "Duties of Physicians," ibid., *36* (June 9, 1847), 381.

70. Worthington Hooker, *Dissertation on the Respect Due to the Medical Profession and the Reasons that it is not awarded by the Community* (Norwich, Conn., 1844), p. 9; Holmes, "Homoeopathy and Its Kindred Delusions," p. 25. Hooker, who was highly sensitive to the changes taking place in the profession, was the professor of medicine at Yale.

and South Carolina resolved to refuse gratuitous treatment to clergymen as long as the latter continued to support quackery.[71] Daniel Drake was impressed by the large number of respectable ministers in Cincinnati who gave support to Thomsonianism.[72]

Thomsonians could usually be relied upon to carry any idea to absurdity. If some respectable ministers found the perfectionist implications of Thomson's doctrine attractive, a more enthusiastic sort was drawn by the eschatological tone of Elias Smith's writings. Something important was at hand, Smith predicted:

> Either the general ruin of all nations, or the downfall of all *anti-christian* powers, to prepare the way for the second coming of the Son of Man, that great voices in heaven may proclaim 'the kingdoms of this world are become the kingdom of our Lord and of his Christ, and he shall reign forever and ever.' God grant this may be the event of all the present commotion in the earth, even so, Amen.[73]

Orthodox physicians called attention to the spirit of radicalism that was disrupting religion as well as medicine. The similarity in tone between Thomsonianism and millennialism led the *Boston Medical and Surgical Journal* (Dec. 29, 1847) to conclude it "not improbable that the *moral effect* of a long-continued belief in Thomson's absurd and irrational theory, may, like *fanaticism in religion,* often result in practical insanity."

Only frail barriers separated belief in human perfectibility from assertion of the imminence of the thousand-year rule of the saints and the latter from pre-millennialism. Even the cautious Jonathan Edwards had suggested the Great Awakening was to be the dawning of the happy state of God's church on earth. Charles Grandison Finney, by replacing Edwards' emphasis on universal corruption with an enumeration of particular sins, stimulated interest in perfectionism. The zealous preacher could persuade his congregation to abandon intemperance and Sabbath-breaking and thus bring men to the threshold of limitless perfection. But the enthusiasm generated

71. "Ministers and Doctors," *Boston Med. Surg. J.,* *50* (March 29, 1854) , 188; *Minutes of Proceedings of the South Carolina Medical Association at its Annual Meeting, February 1849–50* (Charleston, 1850) , p. 20.

72. Drake, "The People's Doctors," p. 407.

73. Smith, *Life,* p. 354.

by revivals could not readily be contained. Perfectionism created a pitch of expectation which, if unfulfilled, could well lead to affirmation that the rule of the saints would be born of the apocalyptic second coming. This was the creed of William Miller. The road taken by Millerism followed the same route traveled by Thomsonianism, slowly west from Vermont and New Hampshire through the Mohawk Valley into the "burned-over" district.[74] Nowhere was Thomsonianism so successful in its early days as in western New York; nowhere did more botanic colleges spring up than in Rochester, where in 1830 Finney reaped his most abundant harvest.[75] It was observed with good reason in 1847 that "the zealous advocates of new systems of physic are generally those who have an abiding faith in mesmerism, believe in 'live forever Jones' and *had* a strong proclivity toward Millerism." [76] Capacity to ride furiously a variety of hobbyhorses was the hallmark of the Thomsonian mentality.

Just as Thomsonianism had unified the strands of feminism and sentimentalism in its appeal to the "fairer and more gentle portion," so it attracted a broad spectrum of ministers whose cooperation might seem incongruous. In respect to demeanor and education a considerable distance separated the revivalist from the located minister who thought the revival a useful addition to God's work. But both types shared an optimistic approach to the universe which attracted them to Thomsonianism. To intellectuals—Transcendentalists and Unitarians—in advance of popular thought, Thomsonianism could say little. But in town congregations of industrious artisans and struggling lawyers and in village churches throughout the country, as well as on the anxious bench, it won support.

Samuel Thomson never resolved the contradiction between insisting that his cures were the work of genius and claiming that restoration of health would inevitably follow treatment by his system. In practice this led him to expound his system through journals but to oppose the establishment of medical colleges. Less impressed

---

74. Whitney Cross, *The Burned-over District: The Social and Intellectual History of Enthusiastic Religion in Western New York, 1800–1850* (Ithaca, 1950) , pp. 287–88.

75. Thomson, *Narrative*, p. 169; "Report from Rochester," *Boston Med. Surg. J.*, 50 (March 15, 1854) , 135–36.

76. *Boston Med. Surg. J.*, 36 (March 10, 1847) , 182.

with the ability of ordinary people to comprehend even simple medical principles, his followers ultimately resolved the contradiction by ignoring Thomson's "green thumb" convictions and advocating formal education. Every man could still be his own physician, "but not every man a physician to practice generally." [77] As Thomsonian arteries hardened, botanic journals began crude expositions of anatomy and physiology, subjects disdained by Thomson. In several states Thomsonian licensing boards were set up and Thomsonian colleges chartered. The movement was rent asunder in 1838. Alva Curtis led a majority of Thomsonians under the new banner of education; Thomson retained a loyal following to which book learning remained anathema. With Thomson's death in 1843 the old Thomsonians disintegrated and were largely absorbed by Curtis' neo-Thomsonians (or Physio-Medicals, as they came to be called). After 1850, neo-Thomsonians suffered a decline in strength because of Eclectic inroads.

The entire botanic movement, however, was fast losing its crusading fervor and becoming more a pseudo-scientific cult. Eclecticism remained an annoyance to orthodox medicine until the early twentieth century, but the successful assault on medical licensing in New York was to mark the apex of botanic popularity. Worthington Hooker observed these changes in 1849, noting that they were giving Thomsonianism "a very different character from that which it exhibited when it first came in its stern simplicity from the rude hand of its founder." Its popularity, he concluded, "is already declining" and it "will probably soon pass away, to give place to some other kindred delusion." [78]

LOOKING BACKWARD

Thomsonianism has sometimes been viewed simply as a medical expression of the individualist creed of the thirties. But to do the sect justice its continuity with colonial practice must be underscored. Had the people who formed the rank and file of the friendly botanic societies been alive in the mid-eighteenth century, they probably would have been occasional practitioners, but with a difference. The colonial domestic practitioner rarely claimed to be

77. *So. Bot. J., 1* (Oct. 28, 1837), 316–17; ibid., *2* (Aug. 4, 1838), 184–86.
78. Hooker, Worthington, *Physician and Patient* (New York, 1849), p. 119.

able to cure all diseases or to have a theory of medicine. His cures were the result of cunning, a knack in certain types of illness. But with the rise of perfectionism disease became intolerable. It seemed impossible that a benevolent God would ruthlessly consign the greater portion of mankind to protracted pain. Thomson's contribution lay in harnessing this perfectionist ardor to the realities of a still rural society where a great deal of medical practice was inevitably domestic. For all its crudity, Thomsonianism was, in a way, scientific. While the straightforward style and comprehensible vocabulary of the *New Guide to Health* placed it in a class with William Buchan's *Domestic Medicine,* the major eighteenth-century treatise on family practice, the *Guide's* monistic pathology bore a startling resemblance to the pathologies accepted by most orthodox physicians of the day. The transitional nature of the sect was even more graphically illustrated by the contrast, not to say contradiction, between Thomson's claim, typical of the domestic practitioner, that his cures were the work of genius and his insistence, typical of the scientific physician, that restoration of health would inevitably follow treatment by his course.

Regular physicians had thrown down the gauntlet in the 1780s when they began to insist that a license not only commended some but excluded others. In doing this they had raised the question of the need for a medical profession, confident of an affirmative answer. To their amazement Thomson took up the challenge and demonstrated to the satisfaction of many that the capacity of Americans to survive between 1630 and 1760 without a medical profession had not been an accident, that a separate class of medical men was a luxury incompatible with sound reasoning or democratic practice. When one reviews the artificial and contrived nature of the attempt to impose a medical hierarchy in the late eighteenth century—the almost mindless emulation of the worst aspects of British medical institutions—the most notable aspect of Samuel Thomson's career was the fact that he had at least as firm a grasp on the realities of American medical practice as that of his adversaries.

FIVE

Homoeopathy and Its
"Kindred Delusions"

Nous avons changé tout cela, et nous faisons maintenant la médecine d'une methode toute nouvelle.

Reply of Sganarelle to a patient's quibble that he has located the heart on the right side and the liver on the left.
Molière, *Le Médecin malgré lui*, II,iv

SAMUEL HAHNEMANN

In all likelihood Hooker had one eye on homoeopathy when he prognosticated the rise of a "kindred delusion" to replace Thomsonianism. Homeopathy had already made its presence felt in the East and was spreading rapidly into other areas. Its founder, Samuel Christian Hahnemann, was born on April 30, 1755, at Meissen in Saxony. A curious and ambitious youth, he sufficiently impressed his father with his search for knowledge that he was sent to study in Leipsig. His early enthusiasm was for language and literature, but Hahnemann found time to attend medical lectures and soon secured an appointment to a Baron Bruckenthal. In the quiet of his patron's library he augmented his already formidable stock of knowledge and began to yearn for greater challenges. Taking leave of the baron in 1779 he returned to Leipsig and there secured his Doctorate of Medicine in 1780.[1]

The orthodox practice of his day impressed Hahnemann as too uncertain to be scientific, but the road from disillusioned physician to medical reformer was not to be quickly traversed. After practicing his profession in Saxony and Transylvania for a number of years, he was back in Leipsig by 1789, busying himself with a translation

1. William H. King, ed., *History of Homoeopathy and Its Institutions in America* (4 vols. New York, 1905), *1*, ch. 2.

132

of the materia medica of William Cullen of Edinburgh. Hahnemann's curiosity about certain statements made by Cullen led him to study the effects on himself of Peruvian bark. From this and subsequent experiments he concluded that the most effective medicines were those that induced symptoms similar to those of the disease. This doctrine, *similia similibus curantur,* had had a long history. Hahnemann's originality lay in the systematic framework in which he set it.

In 1810 the *Organon of the Homoeopathic Art,* the most complete of his expositions, was published. Searching for a rational explanation for the efficacy of like remedies, Hahnemann hit upon a form of vitalism. Disease, he argued, was not a separate entity affecting a specific organ but a derangement of the "immaterial vital principle" pervading and animating the body. Because vitality is invisible, its morbid disturbances could be perceived only by analyzing symptoms, but these were never to be confused with disease itself.[2]

Disease arose from three "chronic miasms" which disordered vitality: internal syphilis, internal sycosis, and, greater and far more important than either of these, psora.[3] The last was so pernicious that, with the modern refinement in personal habits and attempts to repel skin infections by external remedies, psora had come to reveal itself not only in skin diseases but in all forms of insanity, epilepsy, bone-softening, deafness, asthma, and pains of every kind (p. 141). Despite Hahnemann's efforts, psora was usually dismissed by orthodox physicians and the less refined as "the itch" and was quietly interred by most American homoeopaths.[4]

Having established vitalism as his major premise, Hahnemann returned to *similia similibus* in the *Organon.* The deranged vital principle possesses the capacity to expel morbid disturbances, but its natural tendency to restoration is temporarily paralyzed by disease. To initiate the curative process it is necessary to afflict the system with a more intense but similar disease, a sort of straw man, whose presence spurs the vital principle to new efforts (p. 107).

Hahnemann went on to assert that the way to achieve greater

2. Third American ed., New York, 1849, pp. 99–101.
3. Ibid., p. 140. Sycosis is an inflamatory disease affecting the hair follicles.
4. Oliver Wendell Holmes, "Homoeopathy and Its Kindred Delusions," *Medical Essays: 1842–1882, 9* in Writings of Oliver Wendell Holmes (Boston, 1891), 49.

intensity in the similar disease was to administer diluted doses. Although he insisted that dilution increased the potency, many American homoeopaths remained unconvinced and defended attenuation on completely different grounds. It was necessary to hurry the original disease to "maturity," they claimed, so that vitality could cast it from the body. Attenuated doses alone accomplished this, since their effects were mild in contrast to orthodox drugs which threw the system into chaos just at the critical moment.[5]

Though homoeopathy was not without its schisms, they were infrequent. There was a vagueness on key points built into the system. Hahnemann, for example, usually spoke of vitality as a spiritual principle, a soul. But some of his followers described it in purely material terms, as the sum of physiological processes. At times the same writer used both descriptions without awareness of inconsistency. "A disease is neither physical nor chemical, but essentially a vital phenomenon," Augustus Biegler asserted in 1843. But on the same page he claimed that health was restored "by the physiological reaction of nature itself." [6] Though homoeopathic pathology began with derangement of vitality, Hahnemann was more concerned with symptoms and confined his account of psora to a catalogue of its manifestations rather than an analysis of its nature. In the same spirit Alexis Eustaphieve, a Russian immigrant and popularizer of homoeopathy in America, condemned the "presumptuous search after vitality, 'vis medicatrix,' or by whatever name the inscrutable principle of life may have been designated." [7] The inscrutability of the vital principle, in other words, was of no special consequence as long as one believed that disease was due to its disordering, not an entity in itself. Biegler's contradiction went unnoticed, partly because homoeopaths were not really interested in describing the ultimate principle, partly because, when they did, they usually used the term "nature." Nature could be spiritual or material; it could refer to the physiological processes or to a nonmaterial force that imbued the body, like fire to Luther's iron, or to a force altogether outside the body which beneficently restored health.

5. Alexis Eustaphieve, *Homoeopathia Revealed* (New York, 1846), p. 25; Augustus Biegler, *A Discourse on Allopathia and Homoeopathia* (Rochester, 1843), pp. 24–25. The "öo" in homoeopathy was rendered in English in a variety of ways. In the text it will be expressed "oeo" regardless of the usage of the author quoted.

6. Biegler, *A Discourse on Allopathia and Homoeopathia*, pp. 23–24.

7. Eustaphieve, *Homoeopathia Revealed*, pp. 24–25.

Homoeopathy made its appearance in America long before its founder's death in 1843. The first American homeopath of any importance, Hans Burch Gram, was born in Boston in 1788, the son of a Danish immigrant who had been disinherited for an indiscreet marriage to the daughter of a Boston innkeeper. After his father's death Gram sailed to Copenhagen in 1806 to obtain his share of the family fortune. Successful in obtaining a portion of his grandfather's legacy, Gram then conceived an interest in studying medicine. Through his uncle, a physician-in-ordinary to the king, he was placed in the Royal Medical and Surgical Institute. Shortly after graduation Gram was introduced to the theories of Hahnemann, and by the time of his return to America in 1825 he was a convinced homoeopath.[8]

Gram opened an office in New York but was more devoted to cultivating homoeopathy in the fertile soil of America than to treating patients. A few months after he settled there he attempted to popularize the new creed by publishing an infelicitous and generally unread translation of Hahnemann's *Geist der homoeopathischen Heil-lehre*. More profitable were the contacts he made through his membership in a Masonic lodge and the New York County medical society. His first convert was John F. Gray, a former pupil of Hosack, who was won over by Gram's success in curing a seemingly incurable dyspeptic. Another former student of Hosack, Abraham D. Wilson, was next to embrace homoeopathy. Wilson was the son of Peter Wilson, at whose academy in Hackensack Hosack and other prominent figures in the profession had studied. It was probably a measure of their long-standing association with Hosack that the homoeopathic converts were not driven from the county society.[9]

The conversion in 1832 of William Channing, a nephew of William Ellery Channing, occasioned the first division in American homoeopathy. With the great majority of Europeans Channing held to "Hahnemannism pure and simple," rejecting recourse to the orthodox materia medica under any circumstances, while Gram, Gray, and Wilson were willing to consult orthodox manuals in the absence of a similium for a disease.[10] The greater flexibility of

8. King, *History of Homoeopathy*, *1*, 60. Gram was no relation to H.C.J. Gram, the famous Danish bacteriologist.

9. Ibid., p. 61; John F. Gray, *Early Annals of Homoeopathy in New York* (New York, 1863), pp. 11–15.

10. Gray, *Early Annals*, pp. 18–20.

Gram's circle provides another clue to the tolerance of the county society.

The second direct line in the introduction of homoeopathy to America was due to the immigration of a number of German-speaking physicians to Pennsylvania. The first of these was Henry Detweiler, a Swiss naturalist, who had intended to settle among the Indians and study their remedies. On arriving at Philadelphia in 1817 he was dissuaded from this ambition and resolved to settle at Hellertown. There he became acquainted with William Wesselhoeft.

Political reasons were chiefly responsible for the latter's immigration. A medical student of Jena, Wesselhoeft was acquainted with Friedrich Ludwig Jahn, the "father of gymnastics," and had played a role in the *Burschenschaften* (radical student fraternities). But his political activities were more exciting than successful. Thrown into prison, he managed to escape and for some time remained concealed in his father's house. His elaborate plans to aid the Germans fighting for Greek independence met with frustration, and Wesselhoeft decided to come to America. In Germany he had met Charles Follen, later the professor of German literature at Harvard, and George Ticknor, a young Boston scholar with an enthusiasm for Continental languages. They urged Wesselhoeft to settle in Boston and establish a gymnasium, but he preferred Northampton County in Pennsylvania. Through correspondence with German friends, Wesselhoeft learned of Hahnemann and began to experiment with homoeopathic remedies, communicating his results to Detweiler. By the early thirties both were confirmed in their support of the homoeopathic movement.

Detweiler and Wesselhoeft had their homoeopathy at second hand, but they were soon joined by a homoeopath of impeccable credentials, Constantine Hering. Hering was the son of a village organist near Dresden who, it was said, greeted the news of Constantine's birth with a rendition of *Nun danket Alle Gott*. Political authorities, however, found little cause for elation in the younger Hering's enthusiasm for democracy. Perhaps suspecting that the lot of a democrat in Saxony was not a happy one, Hering took refuge in intense scientific study. By the time of his graduation as Doctor of Medicine from Würzburg in 1826, Hering's homoeopathic proclivities were well known. Sent by the King of Saxony on a botanical and zoologi-

cal expedition to Surinam and Cayenne, he expanded his understanding of Hahnemann's doctrines by practicing on the natives and
contributed papers to a homoeopathic journal. When these were
brought to the attention of the royal physician, orders were sent that
Hering should cease medical hypothesizing and attend to his zoological duties. This was too much for the insubordinate young man.
Convinced that a free people would more readily discern the merit
of homoeopathy, and learning that some German immigrants had
established an academy of natural science in Philadelphia, he dis-
patched his botanical and zoological collection to it and arrived in
that city himself in 1833.[11]

Although there were then only ten homoeopaths in the entire
state, Hering quickly set to work obtaining a charter for a homoeopathic college in Allentown. Incorporated in 1835, the Allentown
Academy paved the way for the establishment in 1848 of the Homoeopathic College of Pennsylvania, the most important of the
sect's colleges before 1860.[12]

HOMOEOPATHY IN AMERICA

The first phase in the expansion of homoeopathy in America
lasted from 1825 to 1835. The doctrine was introduced in only two
states and in neither did it attract much of a following. The reasons
for this are not difficult to find. Most American physicians could
not read German, and the few references to Hahnemann they could
cull from British journals were less than flattering. By 1841, however, homoeopathy had won support in most states and was on its
way to becoming a major medical sect.

A variety of factors contributed to this sudden acceptance. In 1833
French translations of Hahnemann's *Materia Medica Pura* and of
Gottlieb Jahr's *Manual of Homoeopathic Medicine,* a popularization
of Hahnemann's theories, gave new impetus to the movement.[13]
The faculty of the Allentown school was busy translating the *Or-
ganon,* while its graduates carried the new system throughout the

11. King, *History of Homoeopathy, 1,* 74–75, 128–142.
12. Frederick C. Waite, "American Sectarian Medical Colleges before the Civil
War," *Bull. Hist. Med., 19* (Feb. 1946), 162–63. The full title of the Allentown
Academy—the North American College of the Homoeopathic Healing Art—was rarely
used.
13. Gray, *Early Annals,* pp. 22–23.

East and Midwest. Meanwhile, a steady flow of incoming European homoeopaths continued, thus keeping the American wing in constant touch with Continental developments.

In New York homoeopathy moved slowly up the Hudson Valley to the Mohawk and thence in a westerly direction. Its dissemination was gradual, county by county, and it was not until 1849 that the Central New York Homoeopathic Medical Society was organized at Utica. More rapid progress was made in Massachusetts. In 1838 a convert from orthodox practice, Samuel Gregg, began to employ homoeopathic methods in Boston. Two years later nine homoeopathic physicians met at the house of J. P. Spooner in Dorchester to organize a "Homoeopathic Fraternity." Their number was augmented by twenty-five converts in the next decade.[14]

At about the time that homoeopathy was gaining ground in Massachusetts a pupil of Hahnemann, William Sturm, began homoeopathic practice in Cincinnati. But the sect made only modest advances in Ohio before 1849. The inability of orthodox physicians to ameliorate suffering during the cholera epidemic of that year caused widespread desertion from orthodox ranks. A thousand physicians and interested laymen organized a homoeopathic society in Cincinnati and in 1850 a homoeopathic college was established in Cleveland.[15]

Through Ohio homoeopathy was carried to the West and South. William H. Holcombe, originally of Lynchburg, Virginia, embraced it while he was in Cincinnati and during the fifties gained a reputation by his practice in Natchez and northern Louisiana. At New Orleans an indigenous movement had sprung up among French-speaking physicians whose journal, *L'Homoion,* was the most popular French medical periodical in the city's history.[16]

Much of homoeopathy's success was undoubtedly due to its cooperation with Eclectic medicine. The Eclectic Medical Institute in Cincinnati had a chair in homoeopathic medicine, though it had to be abolished in 1850 when its holder began to convert not only students but faculty members as well. Frequently, homoeopaths

14. King, *History of Homoeopathy, 1,* 49, 210–11.
15. Ibid., 171–72, 177.
16. John Duffy, ed., *The Rudolph Matas History of Medicine in Louisiana* (2 vols. New Orleans, 1959, 1962), 2, 35–37.

mingled Eclectic remedies with their own, a practice that grew more common despite objections by purists.

The popularity of homoeopathy in areas in which Thomsonianism flourished has led some to conclude that it arose out of the ruins of the latter. In this view the enthusiasm which had created the friendly botanic societies found a new outlet in homoeopathy; the same people, or families, formed the doctors and patients of each movement.[17] There is some evidence for this conclusion in addition to geographical coincidence.

The apology of homoeopathy was based on the alleged conformity of its methods to the laws of nature. "We Homoeopathic physicians," Edward Bayard of New York wrote, "abjure Allopathia for this—she ignores nature and her powers, in her practice violates her, and in her place sets up the supremacy of her own art." [18] While the "allopaths" did violence to nature with their heroic doses, homoeopaths sought only to strengthen the natural tendency to restoration. This assumed that nature was beneficent, that it worked for the best and had best be let alone. From this premise homoeopaths drew the "consolatory doctrine" that any disease could be cured if a *similium* could be found, a conclusion which dispelled "the stupid dogma of the uncertainty of medicine." [19] Optimistic clergymen were drawn to this view, which made disease less an inexplicable visitation of divine wrath, more a predictable outcome of disregard for nature's laws, and were as enthusiastic in their support of homoeopathy as they had been for Thomsonianism. Hahnemann, like Thomson, was often spoken of as a prophet, "the new Evangelist," the "most inspired of discoverers." Religion itself, a British writer asserted in 1850, "has undergone a spiritual revolution since the date of Hahnemann's discovery." When the old system of medicine had given way before the tide of homoeopathy, a clergyman concluded, "then, *for the first time,* will the Gospel of the Kingdom of Grace be preached, as Jesus ordered it to be preached, and received as God ordered it to be received." To the *British Journal of*

17. Frederick C. Waite, "Thomsonianism in Ohio," *Ohio State Archaeol. Hist. Q.,* *49* (Oct.–Dec. 1940) , 330.

18. Edward Bayard, *Homoeopathia and Nature and Allopathia and Art* (New York, 1858) , p. 3; called allopathy from "allos" (other) as opposed to "homoios" (like) .

19. John Epps, *Homoeopathy and Its Principles Revealed* (London, 1850) , pp. 64–65.

Homoeopathy Hahnemann's doctrines formed "not a science merely, but also, for those who comprehend it, a sublime devotion, a form of religion, a rainbow of divine union, holding out to mankind the promise of speedy regeneration." [20]

Yet, despite the support of clergymen for both movements, and despite the already noted facts of geographical coincidence and the conversion of some Eclectic physicians to homoeopathy, this sect did not derive its primary impetus from the collapse of Thomsonianism.

Thomsonianism was dying by 1840 as the iconoclastic spirit that had produced it began to wane. By the time homoeopathy reached the burned-over district, Thomsonianism had burned out. Neo-Thomsonianism had only a short life before being engulfed by Eclecticism, and both sects were more sophisticated than the simple creed of Samuel Thomson. Further, the assertion that homoeopathy thrived only in areas formerly swept by Thomsonianism, "in exactly these areas and no others," does violence to the map. [21] Botanic medicine never made a strong impression in Pennsylvania and New York City, the centers of homoeopathy. In Vermont and New Hampshire where Samuel Thomson had first attracted attention there were fewer than twenty-five homoeopathic doctors before 1850. Homoeopathy was practically unknown in South Carolina and rural Georgia where the Thomsonians had secured repeal in the thirties; its strongest center in the South was New Orleans where Thomsonianism was not a major force. Even in areas attracted to both movements, Ohio and eastern Massachusetts, the majority of homoeopaths (and nearly all the important ones) were either recent immigrants or converts from regular practice. [22] Not until after 1850 was the movement taken over by graduates of homoeopathic colleges. Evidence that Thomsonians went over en masse to homoeopathy is scant and likely to remain so, for, despite superficial similarities, homoeopathy had a radically different spirit than Thomsonianism.

Although Alva Curtis had dabbled in both phrenology and mesmerism, his motivation was more iconoclastic than philosophical. Not only was there no intrinsic relationship between Thomsonian-

20. Quoted in Dan King, *Quackery Unmasked* (New York, ca. 1858), pp. 137–41.
21. Waite, "Thomsonianism in Ohio," p. 330.
22. King, *History of Homoeopathy*, *1*, 267–68, 293–94, 334–36, and passim.

ism and phrenology or mesmerism but none was ever asserted. In its treatment of phrenology and mesmerism homoeopathy suggested its different tone.

"We had other topics besides homoeopathy," Gray wrote of Hans Gram's circle in New York, "in which we derived deeply interesting instruction from Gram." These were the discoveries of Mesmer and the craniology of Gall:

> In each of these directions Gram led the way to a wider and deeper knowledge of the relations between soul and body, the human and divine, the transitory and the permanent, than can be entertained by purely materialistic researches.[23]

Hahnemann had discoursed briefly on mesmerism at the conclusion of the *Organon*, claiming that none but madmen could doubt its efficacy. Specifically, he cited four homoeopathic uses for mesmerism. By varying the firmness with which he ran his hands over the body of a mesmerized patient, the mesmerist could incite symptoms analogous to those of the disease, achieve a balance of vital power throughout the system, restore vital power to a weak part, or, finally, draw off an excess of vitality. More significant than the particulars of his treatment was the manner in which Hahnemann reconciled matter and spirit. He insisted that men with *"very moderate inclination for sexual intercourse"* were best suited as mesmerists. In their case "an abundance of the subtle vital energy, which would also be employed in the secretion of semen, is disposed to communicate itself to other men through the medium of touch, seconded by a strong intention of the mind." Vitality, though spiritual, could thus flow from matter and be transmuted back to matter by a combination of physical manipulation and mental concentration.

The way in which homoeopathy dealt with the relationship of matter and spirit is at once its most confusing and important aspect. The confusion arises from the lack of precision with which Hahnemann's followers described vitality; the importance comes from the fact that homoeopathy appealed to a wide segment of the American intelligentsia in the forties, not in spite of its vagueness but because

23. Gray, *Early Annals*, pp. 21–22.

of it. Disillusionment with the tidy categories of eighteenth-century empiricism, nurtured by the influx of German idealistic philosophy, was creating a desire for a more profound approach to the mind–body problem. Indicative of this yearning was the tendency of people drawn to homoeopathy to espouse also mesmerism and phrenology, into which they read a far greater spiritual content than either possessed.[24]

Anton Mesmer had made his major discoveries in animal magnetism in the 1780s, but his ideas had a special fascination for intellectuals in the 1840s. The capacity of one person to influence the physical actions of another through mental concentration seemed further corroboration of a unified view of reality which had been gaining strength from a variety of sources.

In the early nineteenth century, England had been the scene of a number of clashes among disciples of John Hunter, the eighteenth-century anatomist and surgeon who had collected 13,000 specimens from animal and human life for deposit in the Hunterian Museum of the Royal College of Surgeons. In 1814 John Abernethy, a noted London surgeon, delivered a series of lectures on anatomy before the College in which he expounded his views of Hunter's doctrines. According to Abernethy, Hunter was a convinced vitalist, holding that life was superadded to bodily structure and depended on a subtle substance, similar to but not identical with electricity.[25] Abernethy was sharply criticized by William Lawrence, his pupil, a lecturer at the College, and *enfant terrible* of the profession. Lawrence did not dispute Abernethy's interpretation of Hunter (though it was by no means clear from his published writings that Hunter

24. The president of Union College in Schenectady, Benjamin Joslin, was a convert of Gray and with most professors at the college a staunch advocate of mesmerism; see Charles Morley, *Elements of Animal Magnetism* (New York, ca. 1845). In nearby Albany two of the leading homoeopaths, Henry Paine and Charles Hoffendahl, were mesmerists; see ibid., and King, *History of Homoeopathy, 1,* 84, 94. Contemporaries noted the fondness of proponents of mesmerism for homoeopathy; see "Relations between the Clerical and Medical Professions," *Boston Med. Surg. J., 38* (July 26, 1848), 518.

25. John Abernethy, "An Enquiry into the Probability and Rationality of Mr. Hunter's Theory of Life," *Introductory Lectures, Exhibiting Some of Mr. Hunter's Opinions Respecting Life and Diseases, Delivered before the Royal College of Surgeons, London, in 1814 and 1815* (new ed. London, 1822), pp. 71, 73; Owsei Temkin, "Basic Science, Medicine, and the Romantic Era," *Bull. Hist. Med., 37* (March–April 1963), 98ff.

held the views ascribed to him), but he insisted that using the vital principle as an explanation for life was unscientific. If vitality was taken to mean a spiritual or animating principle, or even an invisible material fluid, then science was being forced into the realm of the unverifiable; speculation about vitality did not explain how the thing takes place, it was merely a mode of stating the fact:

> To say that irritability is a property of living muscular fibres, is merely equivalent to the assertion that such fibres have in all cases possessed the power of contraction. What then is the cause of irritability? I do not know and cannot conjecture.[26]

"Vitality" for Lawrence was thus at best a descriptive, and at worst a tautological term—a statement that living things were alive.

Coleridge, coming to Abernethy's defense, identified Lawrence's opinions with those of the French physiologist Bichat, who defined vitality as the sum of forces resisting death, a definition Coleridge alternately condemned as tautological and the "vilest form of modern materialism." [27] The latter charge was inaccurate. Lawrence was an empiricist in the tradition of Hume, not a mechanist. Given the state of scientific learning in the second decade of the nineteenth century, Lawrence could no more explain life in physical and chemical terms than Abernethy could by a vital principle. Lawrence had to fall back on a cosmic agnosticism that satisfied no one. Speculation about a vital principle was bad science but at least an explanation. Lawrence found himself increasingly isolated, while most scientists followed Abernethy in seeking answers to the ultimate questions in physiology.[28]

In 1840 Joseph Green, Coleridge's disciple and physician, carried

26. William Lawrence, *Lectures on Physiology, Zoology, and the Natural History of Man, Delivered at the Royal College of Surgeons* (London, 1822), pp. 71, 73, and passim; G. J. Goodfield, *The Growth of Scientific Physiology: Physiological Method and the Mechanist-Vitalist Controversy, Illustrated by the Problems of Respiration and Animal Heat* (London, 1960), ch. 5.

27. Kathleen Coburn, ed., *The Philosophical Lectures of Samuel Taylor Coleridge, Hitherto Unpublished* (London, 1949), p. 356. Coleridge might have said "purest form."

28. Temkin, "Basic Science, Medicine, and the Romantic Era," pp. 115–23.

the vitalist position even farther in a Hunterian oration before the College. He marked his theme by quoting Schelling's dictum that the philosophical anatomist "should strive to apprehend the symbolic character of all organic forms, and to learn that in every particular a universal form, and in every outward an inward type, is revealed." Green had studied in Berlin and was heavily influenced by an imaginative if eccentric school of German thought known as nature philosophy. As typified by the anatomist Lorenz Oken, nature philosophy posited that all organic forms were but modifications of one primary form. Animals were thus fetal stages of man, the osseous system a repetition of a simple vertebra. Green lent a ready assent to this creed, arguing that Hunter's anatomical collection was a confirmation of nature philosophy, since it exhibited "every order of living beings . . . as so many embryonic states of an Organism, to which nature from the beginning has tended." Hunter never clearly stated his goal in assembling his collection, but Green was certain that the collection proved that nature was "laboring in birth with man," that man was the "ultimate aim and consummation of nature." [29]

Green was well acquainted with the work of Michael Faraday. Faraday's demonstration that all the varieties of electricity—frictional, voltaic, galvanic, magnetic, and thermal—were fundamentally identical had left only doubts about "how few of the phaenomena and changes of nature" would be left unexplained by electricity in the future. It was characteristic of the intellectual climate of the 1840s that others were eager to credit Faraday with the same idealistic twist that Green had imputed to Hunter.

Faraday knew of Mesmer's work, but his cautious temper saved him from plunging into the labyrinth of animal electricity. Not so Baron Charles von Reichenbach, a German chemist and metallurgist of some repute who attempted to identify the mesmeric force with physical magnetism. Reichenbach's subjects claimed to see different colored flames emanating from magnets, crystals, and the human body. These emanations, Reichenbach insisted, were capable of producing sensations of heat or cold. He termed this phenomenon the

29. Joseph Henry Green, *Vital Dynamics: The Hunterian Oration before the Royal College of Surgeons in London, 14th February, 1840* (London, 1840), p. 38. Hunter's real intentions, especially with respect to his collection, are known only at second hand from nineteenth-century commentators like Richard Owen and William Clift.

odic or odyle force, but attempts by others to test it were always disappointing. Although his subjects were probably honest, they were often emotionally disturbed women, inordinately responsive to the baron's leading questions.[30]

Despite the dubious scientific merit of his researches, a congenial atmosphere for the reception of Reichenbach's work was provided in Britain by a group of physicians organized around the journal *Zoist*, founded in 1843 by John Elliotson, a censor and lecturer to the Royal College of Physicians and a leader in the launching of University College Hospital. Although animal magnetism had been only one of Reichenbach's concerns, his English translators, John Ashburner and William Gregory—both colleagues of Elliotson and contributors to *Zoist*—made the relevance of the odic force hinge almost entirely on its mesmeric applications. They did this because they were physicians, primarily interested in the therapeutic value of mesmerism, and because, like many physicians of their day, they could not resist slipping into vain musings about the ultimate nature of life as manifested by mesmerism. This dual concern was ultimately to be the downfall of the mesmeric movement. Mesmerism was valuable in certain emotional disorders and as an anesthetic in surgery, but it never fulfilled Elliotson's expectations. The discovery of ether seemed to eliminate its anesthetic relevance, and the acceptance by *Zoist* of Reichenbach's position that the mesmeric force was physical—a sort of invisible fluid—frustrated understanding of its occasional therapeutic success. As its medical functions declined after 1850 (*Zoist* stopped publication in 1856), the legitimate medical uses of mesmerism were lost from view. Attention shifted to fascination with the reveries of the mesmerized clairvoyant. From there the road to Christian Science and spiritualism was all too short. Faraday, who had kept his head, spent his last years scorning Mrs. Browning's invitations to seances. Elliotson, who had not, watched his fondest hopes ruined by the din of table rappings.

30. Charles von Reichenbach, *Researches on Magnetism, Electricity, Heat, Light, Chrystallization, and Chemical Attraction, in Their Relations to Vital Force,* trans. and ed. by William Gregory (London, 1850); Reichenbach, *Physico-Physiological Researches on the Dynamics of Magnetism . . . and Chemism,* trans. and ed. by John Ashburner (1st American ed. New York, 1851). Ashburner used the second German edition, hence the slight difference in titles. See also Frank Podmore, *Mesmerism and Christian Science: A Short History of Mental Healing* (1st American ed. Philadelphia, 1909), p. 157.

But in the forties mesmerism was still in its heyday, valuable to the scientist, intriguing to the layman.

The same combination of genuine interest in experimentation and a propensity to boundless theorizing that revived interest in mesmerism after 1830 nurtured the new psychological system of phrenology, which was an attempt to develop a science of the mind and ultimately of personality. For the phrenologist the mind was composed of some thirty-seven independent faculties, ranging from combativeness to amativeness, each localized in a different region of the brain. The development of these "organs" or faculties determined the size and shape of the cranium, with the corollary that one skilled in the new science could make an accurate analysis of character by examining the contours of the subject's head.

The originator of phrenology was a German physician, Franz Joseph Gall (b. 1758). But Gall was too serious a scientific investigator to dilute his findings for popular consumption. That was the work of his colleague, Johann Gaspar Spurzheim (b. 1776), who carried the new science to America. Spurzheim's untimely death in Boston in 1832 temporarily arrested the spread of phrenology, but the torch was picked up by a Scot named George Combe, who conducted a highly successful lecture tour of the United States between 1838 and 1840. Spurzheim and Combe trimmed Gall's theories of pessimistic implications by ignoring the potentially destructive organs noted by the founder, and by emphasizing the capacity of exercise to improve desirable faculties. The final debasement was carried out in the 1840s by the brothers Orson and Lorenzo Fowler of New York City, who reduced phrenology to the scientific level of palm reading (Orson Fowler liked to travel on trains because he believed the experience charged his body with electrical energy).[31]

Before the quack phase set in, however, phrenology commanded the serious interest and outright support of an impressive galaxy of American intellectuals, including John C. Warren, Walt Whitman, the alienist Isaac Ray, and, predictably, Horace Greeley. The new science was both optimistic and systematic; it penetrated the hitherto locked recesses of the mind and proffered hope to the reformer in an age of uplift. As such it fitted nicely the disposition of a gen-

31. John D. Davies, *Phrenology, Fad and Science: A Nineteenth Century Crusade* (New Haven, 1955), chs. 1, 2–4.

eration of American intellectuals to locate the themes that unified the material and spiritual orders.

The most ambitious product of this redrawing of the bounds of science was written in 1842 by Joseph Rodes Buchanan, a young Kentucky medical student and in later years a leading figure in Eclecticism. His *Sketches of Buchanan's Discoveries in Neurology* was an attempt to weave the threads of phrenology, mesmerism, psychology, and medicine into a uniform fabric.[32] Buchanan's first principle (p. 70) was that:

> every passion or emotion that man can feel; every intellectual faculty that he can exercise, and every function that is performed in any part of his body, has a legitimate origin in some portion of his nervous system. The result of my investigations shows that all of these localities can be ascertained; and such has been my progress, that but few important principles have been left for future discovery.

All muscular movements and spiritual desires, he argued, can be traced to a particular section of the brain through a "pathognomic line" that connected physical and psychic functions. To give a practical illustration (p. 87):

> That portion of the brain which produces the love of habitation, or desire to live in a house, produces also an easy, pleasant condition of the lungs, in which the inspirating, oxygenating functions are arrested or retarded, and the demand for fresh or cool air is very limited, by which condition we are fitted for living in close compartments.

Animating the "pathognomic line" was a nervous fluid. Buchanan described the fluid as electrical and emphasized that it transmitted spiritual affections. Through the agency of animal magnetism the fluid

> is susceptible of being transmitted from one person to another of the proper susceptibility; and in some cases, the action of all intellectual and affective organs may be thus

32. Cincinnati, 1842.

147

transmitted, reproducing in the subject, the sensations, emotions, and thoughts of the operator.

This transmission, he concluded, "may be either through the hand, or by direct radiation from the head" (p. 91).

Despite his best efforts to be scientific in dealing with mesmerism, Buchanan was continually distracted by its sideshow aspects. Much of the *Sketches* is taken up with highly colored accounts of hysterical females under hypnosis. But his work was more than the offshoot of a heated imagination. Pseudo-scientific by twentieth-century standards, in the light of his day it was highly scientific, a crude expression of a widely held desire to unify spiritual and material experience. No name seemed adequate to describe so comprehensive a system. Buchanan, after trying "neurology," "anthropology," and "therapeutic sarcognomy," finally struck upon "moral medicine." The last involved "affecting the body in a beneficial manner by mental influences." Only thus "can Physiognomy be rendered a *Science*" (p. 86).

Buchanan's system, however, could never be wholly acceptable to religious people. Although mesmerism played a major role in the launching of spiritualism, the weight of scientific testimony in the forties still supported the theory that the mesmeric force was an invisible physical fluid. Buchanan argued that, when he spoke of the brain, he included "the spiritual life connected with it."[33] But if spiritual affections could be reduced to electricity for transmission to others, they could hardly be fundamentally different from, or superior to, matter. How could Buchanan affirm in a single breath that spirit "constitutes the true life of man" and that the "science of the brain is the science of man"? In his attempt to overcome the cleavage between mind and body Buchanan was coming dangerously close to materialism.

Even if he could establish the primacy of spiritual affections, however, Buchanan was still leaving very little room for God. "As, in speaking of the earth, or of the universe, the power and existence of

33. "What is Neurology," *Buchanan's Journal of Man*, *1* (Jan. 1849), 8. This journal (quite literally Buchanan's—he wrote every article) contained some of the first expositions of Reichenbach's views for an American audience.

the Diety are understood oftener than expressed," Buchanan wrote, "so, in speaking of the physical constitution of man, the co-existence of his spiritual nature is taken for granted." But this was an unhelpful solution to the problems of religious liberals, clerical and lay, in approaching science in the forties. They had originally welcomed science as a grand highway to perfection, one that would not destroy a moderately latitudinarian interpretation of Scripture. God, intending that man be happy in his material sojourn, had created laws, or rules, whose observance would suffice for His object. Not only would science, by adumbrating the nature of these laws, harmonize with the Bible, but, by increasing the sum total of happiness, it would fulfill God's plan for the universe. Difficulty developed not out of contradiction between science and religion but from a fear that devotion to the former would cause apathy toward religion. Was it enough, in other words, simply to affirm like Buchanan the ultimate congruity of the two? Did not one also have to demonstrate that science could make immediate revelations about divinity? A system reconciling science to religion, not religion to science, was needed. Phrenology and mesmerism both suggested a close relationship of matter and spirit, but only in this world. The mesmeric force never quite transcended the immediate audience. Homoeopathy was, on the surface, little better. It was a science with a spiritual aspect, but it was mute concerning divinity. To resolve their problem, to incorporate the startling discoveries of Gall, Mesmer, and Hahnemann into a genuinely religious framework, liberals turned increasingly to Swedenborgianism.

Emanuel Swedenborg was at once a scientist and a mystic. His interests included physics, biology, chemistry, astronomy, and mineralogy. In the last two fields he made major contributions, anticipating Laplace's hypothesis of the nebular origin of the universe and instituting numerous technical reforms in the Swedish mines. But true to the Enlightenment, he was ever seeking to get beyond phenomenal descriptions to the first principles of matter and motion. He hoped to base all science on mathematics but was not successful. In later life he became increasingly occupied with mystical experiences and claimed direct communication with angels. Swedenborg naturally suited the intellectual climate of America in the forties. Emer-

149

son wrote that Swedenborg "saw and showed the connections between nature and the affections of the soul. He pierced the emblematic or spiritual character of the visible, audible, tangible world." [34] The twentieth century has dismissed Swedenborg's mysticism as an aberration, but to the generation of the 1840s he was all the more scientific because mystical, because he saw nature not as a fixed order but as "the image or shadow of the creative life *in man*." [35] Especially popular in New York and Philadelphia, Swedenborgianism was also a potent force in the later days of the Brook Farm community.

Mesmerists and Swedenborgians found in each other's system added proof of their own. Swedenborg's contact with the "very *penetralia* of the spirit world" became more plausible when one considered the mesmerist's control over his subject's psyche. The ability of a blindfolded and mesmerized person to indicate by name an acquaintance who unexpectedly entered the room seemed to be at once a proof and conclusion of Swedenborg's doctrine that each person possessed a spiritual sphere, foul or pleasant dependent on his righteousness, that brought him into contact with devils or angels. "If Mesmerism is true," the New York editor, George Bush, concluded, "Swedenborg is true." [36] But the reverse proposition was equally compelling.

Homoeopaths, who were unusually susceptible to the lure of mesmerism, were attracted in considerable numbers to Swedenborgianism. Hering, Gram, and many of the early publicists of the sect, immigrant and native, were devout in their belief. Homoeopathy was so popular among New York and Philadelphia Swedenborgians that a question arose whether one could follow Swedenborg and still reject the way of Hahnemann.[37]

34. Ralph Waldo Emerson, "The American Scholar," *Nature: Addresses and Lectures*, vol. 1 in Complete Works (Boston, 1903) , 113.

35. William James, ed., *The Literary Remains of the Late Henry James* (Boston, 1885) , p. 319.

36. George Bush, *Mesmer and Swedenborg; or The Relation of the Development of Mesmerism to the Doctrines . . . of Swedenborg* (New York, 1847) , pp. 56, 69.

37. Gray, *Early Annals*, p. 27; Calvin Kneer, *Life of Hering* (Philadelphia, 1940) , p. 52. "Many of the older homoeopathists were Swedenborgians," King, *History of Homoeopathy*, *1*, 181. Some individuals, more famous as homoeopathic physicians, wrote major Swedenborgian theological and ecclesiological tracts; see Charles J. Hempel, *The True Organization of the New Church, as indicated in the writings of Emanuel Swedenborg, and demonstrated by Charles Fourier* (New York, 1848) . The

An interesting version of the relationship between homoeopathy and Swedenborgianism can be found in the writings of William Henry Holcombe, one of the best known of the earlier homoeopaths. He was born in Lynchburg, Virginia, in 1825, the son of a physician. His father's decision to free his slaves forced the family's removal to Indiana where Holcombe began his medical studies in his father's office. In 1847 Holcombe entered the University of Pennsylvania's medical department and, on graduating, moved to Cincinnati. His three years in that city (1850–52) were to be the most decisive of his life. The relative success of homoeopaths in treating the cholera epidemic left its mark on Holcombe, and he soon became a convert to the new sect. Shortly thereafter he embraced the creed of Swedenborg. Between 1852 and his death in 1893 Holcombe established himself as the leading homoeopath in the Southwest. He settled finally in New Orleans and wrote a number of religious and medical tracts. By far the most important of the latter was the *Scientific Basis of Homoeopathy.*[38]

Faraday's demonstration of the identity of force was for Holcombe the great idea of his age. The subordinate motions of matter are "but the fragments into which the One Universal Agent has been, as it were, prismatically broken." Light, heat, and electricity are not separate entities but states of matter, and one state can be transmuted into another. Unity of force applies as well to vital phenomena; vital and physical phenomena are of the same stuff. The plant or animal, "like the world itself, is an aggregate of molecules and motions, composed of the same material and necessarily subject to the same laws" (pp. 94–97). Specifically, Holcombe contended that nerve impulses are the sources of vitality, and disease simply an abnormal modification of nerve impulses. He called the impulses "undulations" to indicate their electrical nature. The task of the physician was to prescribe similar remedies which, on entering the system,

reference to Fourier is consistent with the fact that many at Brook Farm, and Brook Farm types in general, were interested in homoeopathy. But even in remote states like Wisconsin, homoeopaths took up the cudgels for Swedenborgianism; see Thomas L. Bradford, *Homoeopathic Bibliography of the United States* (Philadelphia, 1892), p. 86. See also Richard De Charms, *A Defense of Homoeopathy against Her New-Church Assailants* (Philadelphia, 1854).

38. Cincinnati, 1852. See also Holcombe's *How I Became a Homoeopath* (Chicago, 1866); *Aphorisms of the New Life* (Philadelphia, 1883); *The Other Life* (Philadelphia, 1871).

emitted undulations which clashed with and destroyed the abnormal nerve undulations. Holcombe called this the "law of interference." Under certain circumstances (p. 232),

> Two waves of water annul each other, two waves of sound produce silence, two undulations of Heat, Light, and Tithonism or Chemical Action, produce respectively cold, darkness, and no action whatever. I believe that upon the same principle two abnormal nerve undulations destroy each other, and of course the morbid states in the peripheries or the symptoms of disease disappear.

Holcombe had a mistaken notion of the action of drugs, and like many Americans he exaggerated the importance of the nervous system in disease. But he was well read in the scientific literature of his day and was probably the most famous homoeopath outside the East. All the more surprising, then, are his theological tracts, replete with descriptions of civil, social, and domestic relations in heaven, accounts of the sexes here and hereafter, speculation about the manner of hell's creation, the devil's personality, and the necessity for purgatory. One is tempted to shrug off his religious creed as irrelevant to his scientific purposes. But it was in fact highly relevant.

The keystone of Holcombe's theology was his belief that the physical body was only a temporary covering for the spiritual body. The spiritual body is not the soul, "but an organic human form composed of indestructible spiritual substances in which the soul or vital principle lives and is finited, differentiated from God and from all other souls." The material body exists within the soul like a circle within a circle. But the spiritual body is itself part of a spiritual world, a place with spiritual physics, botany, anatomy, architecture, government, and even sex. Anyone expecting to enter a realm of pure thought after death is in for a shock, for he will find that the other life, with a few minor exceptions, is a continuation of this one. There will be no physical bodies, hence no reproduction, but "mental" sex, spiritual marriage, and spiritual government.[39] The orthodox Christian belief was that the natural body, after decomposition, would be changed into a spiritual body at the Last Judgment. Holcombe rejected this "revolting" dogma for Swedenborg's conviction that both bodies coexisted from birth, but only one survived after death.

39. Holcombe, *The Other Life*, pp. 39–40, ch. 8.

Behind Holcombe's conversion to Swedenborgianism, however, lay a deeper concern. Just as he wanted a medical system which connected physiology with the other scientific branches, which brought vitality into the realm of Faraday's identical forces, so he embraced Swedenborgianism because he could not imagine a natural body being suddenly transformed into a spiritual one. Suddenness, discontinuity, the inexplicable, found no place in Holcombe's thinking. Like many other homoeopaths, his watchwords were unity, harmony, the predictable. But the desire to unify all aspects of experience, to see each part of nature in harmony with every other part, could too easily lead to materialism. Were our knowledge of Holcombe confined to the *Scientific Basis of Homoeopathy,* the temptation to classify him as a mechanist would be strong. Only by Swedenborgianism could Holcombe reconcile his comprehensive world view with the primacy of spirit. Traditional Calvinism, with its transcendent God inscrutably acting on man, divided matter and spirt, thus making the world too mysterious a place. In the Swedenborgian's world, in contrast, man could find a spiritual truth at every material turn.

The significance of the mutual attraction of homoeopathy and Swedenborgianism did not lie in the numerical strength of the latter. While Swedenborgianism had an appeal to many intellectuals—a number of American writers including Henry James and William Dean Howells were raised in Swedenborgian homes—it never became a major sect. Probably a majority of homoeopaths, moreover, never formally embraced Swedenborgianism. As Emerson noted in his celebrated essay on Swedenborg, there was too much of the cut and dried, the hard and literal, in Swedenborg's mysticism. The importance of the Swedenborgian attraction lay in its thrust. For many thinking Americans in the 1850s Swedenborgianism was moving in the right direction if not always on the right road, toward an ordered and predictable universe, toward a synthesis of matter and spirit. Since homoeopathy was traveling in the same direction, it too basked in the sun of approval.

One could, then, share the main characteristics of the Swedenborgian frame of mind—impatience with a mechanistic approach to the universe, a conviction that nature was an emanation of spirit, a desire to unify experience—and still not become a Swedenborgian. This was the path of Transcendentalism and it should come as no shock to learn that many Transcendentalists, including Theodore Parker, Bronson Alcott, Elizabeth Palmer Peabody, and Thomas Starr King, gave their support to homoeopathy. So too did prominent New England improvers with a mainly perfectionist motivation such as William Lloyd Garrison, Wendell Phillips, Julia Ward Howe, and Thomas Wentworth Higginson.[40] Among Massachusetts homoeopaths William Wesselhoeft was best known to the Transcendentalists and reformers.

Wesselhoeft, the physician of Theodore Parker, was representative of the sort of person for whom homoeopathy was nearly irresistible. An optimist, he held that "health and longevity were the normal state and natural right of the human race; that the healthy body would resist external causes of disease to an incalculable extent." A perfectionist, his entire faith was that universal health would be produced in the future of the human race on earth. Toward this goal Wesselhoeft espoused temperance, gymnastics, and hydropathy as well as homoeopathy. A mystic and metaphysician, he was attracted to mesmerism and Swedenborgianism, and had studied under Oken, the nature philosopher, imbibing his view that "the human was the metropolis of all organizations," the head a repetition of the trunk, the body a microcosm of nature. By virtue of these enthusiasms Wesselhoeft was prepared for homoeopathy,

> which implies that there are occult relations between the imponderable forces that difference the various substances that compose the mineral, vegetable, and animal kingdoms, and the various organs and functions of the human body.[41]

40. King, *History of Homoeopathy*, *1*, 220. Of these, Elizabeth Peabody, the daughter of a homoeopathic physician, was the strongest advocate of the sect. The Brook Farm people liked to meet at her bookshop, partly devoted to homoeopathic medicines and one of the few places in Boston where German and French books could be bought. See Thomas W. Higginson, *Cheerful Yesterdays* (Boston, 1900), pp. 85–86; *William Lloyd Garrison, 1805–1879. The Story of His Life Told by His Children* (4 vols. New York, 1885–89), *4*, 323; Laura E. Richards and Maud H. Eliot, *Julia Ward Howe, 1819–1910* (2 vols. Boston, 1916), *2*, 231; John Weiss, *Life and Correspondence of Theodore Parker* (2 vols. New York, 1864), *1*, 333, *2*, 332.

41. Elizabeth P. Peabody, *Memorial to Dr. William Wesselhoeft, to which is added his last address to the homoeopathic association* (Boston, 1859), pp. 22, 9, 42, 35. With his brother Robert, he conducted a water-cure establishment in Brattleboro, Vt., which was frequented by the pioneer of humane treatment for the insane, Samuel

All these characteristics were shared to a greater or lesser degree by Transcendentalists and social reformers. The latter were almost always temperance advocates and often were interested in dietary reform. The Transcendentalists, fascinated by German idealistic philosophy, found in Wesselhoeft a spirit akin to their own. With more accuracy than charity the *Boston Medical and Surgical Journal* cautioned orthodox physicians to watch "the sisters, male and female, who now spend their time in running after this hydropathic mummery:

> Last year they were equally full of transcendentalism, the year before of homoeopathy, the years before of animal magnetism, Grahamism, phrenology. Next year they will be Fourierites, communists, George Sandists, etc.[42]

To a certain extent homoeopathy appealed to the same type of person attracted by Thomsonianism—perfectionists, faddists, and reformers. But the differences are more significant than the likenesses. The radicals who professed homoeopathy were intensely respectable radicals, more likely to be encountered in a Henry James drawing room than at a Finney revival. If the homoeopath communicated with God, it was usually in the quiet of his study, not amid the chaos of the anxious bench. One learns that Thomsonianism attracted some respectable clergymen, but their names are not so readily discovered. Homoeopathy, in contrast, was an advanced intellectual movement drawing some of the leading contemporary thinkers.

Orthodox medicine was not oblivious to the merit of homoeopathy. Vaccination was, after all, a way of preventing disease by inciting symptoms similar to those of the disease itself. Mercury, "in itself inert, becomes all powerful merely by minute divisions of its particles," a factor viewed as giving plausibility to the doctrine of small doses.[43] More important, orthodox physicians were coming to a greater appreciation of curative powers of nature at the same time that homoeopaths were proclaiming their system superior because it alone gave nature free reign.

Gridley Howe; see Laura E. Richards, ed., *Letters and Journals of Samuel Gridley Howe* (2 vols. Boston, 1909), *2*, 178.

42. "Relations between the Clerical and Medical Professions," *Boston Med. Surg. J.*, *38* (July 26, 1848), 518.

43. Edward Warren, "Homoeopathy," *Boston Med. Surg. J.*, *44* (April 23, 1851), 236–37.

The Concept of Orthodoxy

Orthodox practice during the first quarter of the nineteenth century was generally Brunonian in character. Diseased states were seen as either sthenic, due to inflammation, or asthenic, resulting from a weakening of stimuli (heat, emotion), with consequent imbalance. The former called for "anti-phlogistics"—bleeding and purging; the latter for stimulants like opium. There were variations from this classification in practice. Benjamin Rush, considering the asthenic state as inevitably following from the sthenic, saw disease entirely in terms of capillary tension and advocated heroic phlebotomy. Wags like William Cobbett called Rush's practice "one of those great discoveries which are made from time to time for the depopulation of the earth"; others adopted his monistic pathology. In New England two rival schools, one led by Dr. Gallup and the other by Drs. Miner and Tully, reduced all diseases to sthenic or asthenic.[44] Still others followed the rising star of the French pathologist, F. J. V. Broussais, who trumpeted inflammation of the gastrointestinal tract as the cause of disease. Perhaps the most impressive aspect of this treatment was the capacity of patients to survive despite their medication.

Fairer winds were blowing from Europe by 1830. The Paris School pioneered identification of specific diseases in terms of localized structural pathology and assailed the prevalent ignorance of statistics in evaluating the effects of remedies. In 1825 Pierre Louis culminated six years of study of pulmonary tuberculosis with the publication of his *Recherches anatomico-pathologiques sur la phthisie*. Louis had kept detailed records of the presence or absence of nearly all possible symptoms and incorporated these along with postmortem findings in his work. Although he lacked knowledge of mathematics, even arithmetic was an improvement on ordinary rule-of-thumb practice.[45]

French clinicians were led by their statistics to skepticism about

44. Worthington Hooker, "Rational Therapeutics," *Pub., Mass. Med. Soc., 1* (1860), 161–62.

45. Louis had to contend with the monistic therapy of F. J. V. Broussais who, though he stimulated interest in morbid anatomy, claimed that most diseases were due to gastroenteritis and called for phlebotomy. Broussais' doctrine resembled that of Benjamin Rush. See Esmond R. Long, *A History of Pathology* (Baltimore, 1928), p. 136.

the value of the existing materia medica. Speaking before the Massachusetts Medical Society in 1835 Jacob Bigelow gave the first major American expression of this "nihilism." Bigelow noted the existence of a type of disease he termed "self-limited": [46]

> one which, after it has obtained a foothold in the system, cannot in the present state of our knowledge, be eradicated, or abridged, by art—but to which there is due a certain succession of processes, to be completed in a certain time.

In contrast to the later extension of the category of self-limited diseases and generally more abstract treatment of the problem, Bigelow was cautious and practical. One might suspect a disease to be self-limited when one finds "opposite modes of treatment recommended, and their successes vouched for, by practitioners of authority and veracity." The same suspicion might be attached to cases in which the supposed cure took place "under chance applications, or inconsiderable remedies; as in the empirical modes of practice on the one hand, and the minute doses of the homoeopathic method on the other." The student, encountering the mass of testimony on the side of art, subjected to medical schools which "find it incumbent on them to teach the cures of diseases," emerges with a conviction that if he fails the blame rests with himself. But in time he will come to realize that some diseases are cured by nature alone.

Only a statistical study, in the manner of the Paris School, could determine how far disease was self-limited and how far controllable by art. In keeping with his cautious tone, Bigelow actually placed very few diseases in the self-limited category. Included were certain eruptive fevers like smallpox, erysipelas, measles, and scarlet fever; diseases accompanied by paroxysms like epilepsy, angina pectoris, mania, and asthma; and, finally, morbid affections which pass by metastasis from one part of the body to another, such as gonorrhea and mumps. In this classification there is little that the physician of today would dispute.

Bigelow's assumption that the system ultimately expelled certain diseases was the most important aspect of his medical philosophy. It is one of the ironies of medical history that he came to this view at

46. Jacob Bigelow, "On Self-Limited Diseases," *Med. Communications, Mass. Med. Soc.*, 5 (1830–36), 319–58.

least partly under the influence of Louis, since the latter, by correlating lesions with symptoms, had opened the way to a localized pathology whose corollary was the use of specific remedies. Louis rejected the corollary, not for philosophical reasons but because his statistical analysis had made him dubious of existing drugs. Specific remedies were not adopted in America either, partly because the homoeopathic challenge was forcing physicians to reconsider the role of nature, and partly because the study of morbid anatomy had made little progress there.[47]

The theory that disease was localized, a sort of military invasion directed at specific parts of the body (the liver and bowels being favorite targets) was more popular in Britain. In attacking it Sir John Forbes provided Americans with a forceful restatement and expansion of Bigelow's views. Already prominent for his translation of Laënnec on percussion, Forbes stirred the British profession in two widely circulated works: "Homoeopathy, Allopathy, and 'Young Physic'" which appeared in the *British Journal of Medicine* in 1846, and *Of Nature and Art in the Cure of Disease,* published in 1857. Rejecting the notion of disease as an entity unto itself, an *imperium in imperio,* Forbes argued that it was indistinguishable from the vital action of the system. Disease acts within the body like a constitutional opposition in a parliamentary government, "organized in accord with the existing laws, and still . . . submitting to their sway." [48] In the case of fevers, for example, the poison, on entering the blood stream, "is by it diffused through the whole system, and so directly visits, and perhaps more or less influences, every organ in its structure, or function, or both."

When he came to the role of nature, Forbes showed the lengths to which orthodox physicians were traveling in extolling her "autocracy." Bigelow had listed the self-limited diseases and assumed the remainder susceptible to art. Forbes, in contrast, enumerated only the diseases admitting of specific remedies and asserted that nature was primarily responsible for curing the rest. While quinine was still reliable in some cases of remittent fever, and mercury, citrus

47. For the slow progress of morbid anatomy studies in America, see Richard H. Shryock, *Medicine and Society in America, 1660–1860* (New York, 1960), p. 64.
48. John Forbes, *Of Nature and Art in the Cure of Disease* (New York, 1858), pp. 79–80.

juices, and iodine in syphilis, scurvy, and bronchitis respectively, the physician could do no more than remove obstacles from nature's path in the great proportion of maladies.[49]

New England, fast becoming the bastion of the *vis medicatrix naturae,* welcomed Forbes' ideas with more enthusiasm that had Britain. Since Bigelow's historic address, William Walker had sought to demonstrate "the power of nature in healing compound fractures . . . to be much greater than is generally supposed." [50] In 1846 John Ware argued that opium was not a necessary resort in delirium tremens, and reliance on mercury in iritis was condemned by H. W. Williams.[51] In distant New Orleans, E. H. Barton was growing skeptical of heroic doses in the treatment of yellow fever.[52]

Changes in practice were accompanying theoretical revisions. Worthington Hooker noted in 1860 that a considerable transformation had taken place since 1835. Bleeding was used much less frequently, and opium had replaced calomel and tartar emetic as the favorite remedy. Disturbing remedies in general were much less in evidence. Some orthodox physicians proclaimed that diseases were simply less sthenic in character than formerly; [53] others continued to regard the materia medica as an engine of war for assaulting the hapless patient. But the trend was unmistakable.

Resemblances between the homoeopathic and orthodox awareness of nature's remedial power should not obscure their considerable differences. Although both agreed that disease was a changed mode of vital action, homoeopaths drew the conclusion that, with the cause of disease ascertained, medicine had finally become an exact science. Orthodox physicians, in contrast, adopted the more skeptical tone of Bigelow. No fewer than five reasons for the uncertainty of medicine were proposed by Worthington Hooker in 1849. A disordering of one organ affected others, and often the entire system,

49. Ibid., pp. 213–24.

50. William Walker, "On the Treatment of Compound and Complicated Fractures," *Med. Communications, Mass. Med. Soc.,* 7, 2 ser. *3* (1842–48), Annual Address, 1845, 171–215.

51. Forbes, *Of Nature and Art in the Cure of Disease,* p. 224.

52. Hooker, "Rational Therapeutics," p. 183.

53. Alex Berman, "The Impact of the Nineteenth Century Botanico-Medical Movement on American Medicine and Pharmacy." Ph.D. thesis (University of Wisconsin, 1954), p. 23.

thus complicating the physician's task. Secret or unseen causes were often at work, and some acknowledged causes, such as the miasm in yellow fever, had defied analysis. The existence of self-limited diseases further confused therapeutics. Vomiting, for example, might result from the restorative convulsions of nature or from a deep-seated irritation requiring immediate treatment. Mental factors were present in every illness, making it virtually impossible to separate the effects of drugs from the influence of the psyche. Finally, no two persons were alike; idiosyncrasies, unless previously known to the physician, could well frustrate the most potent remedies.[54]

In the previous year Elisha Bartlett, Osler's "Rhode Island Philosopher," had made the most comprehensive study of the problem in *An Inquiry into the Degree of Certainty in Medicine*.[55] While Hooker deflated the physician's pretensions to certainty, Bartlett was more concerned with proving that some certainty still remained in medical art. Drawing heavily on the research of Louis and Grisolle on pneumonia, Bartlett concluded that art, through bloodletting and antimonials, "lessens the severity of the disease, shortens its duration, and in many instances prevents its termination in death." [56] But even this modest affirmation was quickly followed by reiteration of the "inconsiderable" extent to which art was efficacious beyond doubt. That Bartlett had to devote nearly sixty pages to proving that certainty had not been altogether banished was indicative of the thrust of medical thought.

Bartlett had merely assumed that medicine was generally uncertain. Most orthodox physicians who thought seriously enough about the subject to set pen to pad actually gloried in its uncertainty. "There is not yet one single branch of it complete," a Louisiana physician wrote:

> We cannot be said to have much more than laid the foundation of the science, if indeed we can say as much. Few, if

54. Worthington Hooker, *Physician and Patient; or A Practical View of the Mutual Duties, Relations and Interests of the Medical Profession and the Community* (New York, 1848), pp. 25–49.

55. William Osler, "Elisha Bartlett: A Rhode Island Philosopher," in *An Alabama Student and Other Biographical Essays* (London, 1908), pp. 108–58; Erwin H. Ackerknecht, "Elisha Bartlett and the Philosophy of the Paris Clinical School," *Bull. Hist. Med.*, 24 (Jan.–Feb. 1950), 43–60.

56. Elisha Bartlett, *An Inquiry into the Degree of Certainty in Medicine; and into the Nature and Extent of Its Powers over Disease* (Philadelphia, 1848), p. 55.

any of its laws, are definitely settled, and it will yet require many years of long and laborious research to give the science that precision, settled and positive character, that distinguishes many other sciences.[57]

"Vital force," a reviewer of Forbes concluded, "though a convenient refuge for the idle theorist, is the great perturbative element which renders the results attained by the faithful student of nature approximate rather than precise." [58]

There was more to this than humble beating of the breasts. Homoeopathy alone of all the sects forced regular physicians to rethink the concept of orthodoxy. Thomsonianism was beneath contempt, the embodiment of crude popular delusions. Hydropathy, never well organized, had always been on the sectarian fringe. Phrenology and mesmerism were not mainly concerned with medicine, though medical significance was read into them by some. Homoeopathy, however, was of a different order. Even its sharpest critics conceded that it was the "Aristocracy of Quackery." [59] Unlike hydropathy, it had numerous flourishing medical societies; unlike Thomsonianism, it avoided identification with radical political and social causes, although political and social reformers supported homoeopathy. With its sophistication and scientific approach, homoeopathy was remarkably akin to orthodox medicine. If the former was a sect, was not the latter also? What claim could orthodoxy lay to a special status, a privileged legal position among sects?

The answer usually given was that orthodoxy alone was free from restricting creeds. "As there are now no prevalent theories in medicine, so there are no sects in the profession." The humoralists, solidists, and vitalists had all passed away, never to rise again. Homoeopathy, Worthington Hooker said, "very summarily" included all regular physicians in one great sect labeled "allopathy." But, he protested, "we are no sect. We have no medical creed." [60] In Boston "Medicus" vehemently disavowed

57. R. M. Graham, "Address delivered before the Physio-Medical Society of New Orleans," *New Orleans Med. Surg. J., 4* (Jan. 1848), 452.

58. "Nature and Art in the Cure of Disease," *North American Review, 89* (July 1859), 166.

59. P. W. Leland, "Empiricism and Its Causes," *Boston Med. Surg. J., 47* (Nov. 3, 1852), 292.

60. Worthington Hooker, *The Present Attitude and Tendencies of the Medical Profession* (New Haven, 1852), p. 15.

all such terms to designate our profession; for it is our duty not to acknowledge any pathy, nor adopt any exclusive system, which may have a tendency to contract our views of nature and the laws by which she is governed, but practise, as we do, on those broad principles of science which have been, and may still be, established by the united efforts of the ablest intellects that have existed and labored, from the earliest period to the present time, for the benefit and happiness of mankind.[61]

Provided regular physicians confined themselves to separating the wheat from the chaff in all systems and avoided uncritical acceptance of any one, they could disclaim sectarian labels. Homoeopaths were excluded from orthodox ranks, not for lack of education or sophistication but for dogmatism—hence the portrayal of orthodoxy as wholly undoctrinaire and highly uncertain in its results.

The difficulty with this approach was that in answering one objection it opened the profession to criticism on other grounds. Was not assertion of the nondogmatic nature of orthodoxy simply a polite way of saying that it lacked scientific principles? Orthodox physicians replied that they were scientific because they relied solely on observation and experiment. But cheerleading for Bacon was a weak refutation. First of all, it was hackneyed; no one was against observation. But, more important, observation that did not lead to the establishment of rational and certain principles was "mere empiricism," not science. Although orthodox physicians claimed to draw conclusions by the cautious process of inductive reasoning, the Massachusetts Homoeopathic Society noted,"yet thus far they do not claim to have deduced any fixed principles of action." [62] Homoeopaths were asking orthodoxy not only for more fixed principles than the latter could produce but for more than it desired to expound, or could desire, consistent with its nonsectarian image.

By any contemporary definition, homoeopaths were more "scientific" than orthodox physicians. Science had to be philosophical, and philosophy had to tie matter and spirit into a coherent system

61. "Medicus," *Boston Med. Surg. J., 44* (April 23, 1851) , 240.
62. "Report of a Committee of the Mass. Homoeopathic Society," ibid. (May 7, 1851) , p. 278.

from which correct deductions could be made. Orthodoxy could not come up to so ambitious a conception of science and still be Baconian; and if it abandoned Bacon it became sectarian. To restate the dilemma, either regular physicians built a new system on the ruins of past efforts, in which case they slipped into sectarianism, or they renounced systematization and became "unscientific." In neither case could one justify their privileged legal position.

THE SIGNIFICANCE OF HOMOEOPATHY

The license laws, as noted, were originally aimed at "empirics" and quacks. By 1860, however, medical sects which did not conform to inherited notions about empiricism or charlatanism had arisen. The result was confusion among educated people. Had the laws been as Draconian as sectarians claimed, they would never have been allowed to linger on statute books for so long. The sputtering and inconsistent nature of the drive for repeal can more readily be explained if one views licensing as more pointless than malicious.

By presenting regular physicians with a caricature of themselves, however, homoeopaths rendered the profession a service. If physicians recognized the hyperbole in Oliver Wendell Holmes' suggestion that only the fish would suffer were the materia medica dumped overboard, they were beginning to see its element of truth as well. The popularity of the homoeopaths' mild therapy and small doses helped to bury the fashion of heroic treatment. Many regular physicians, moreover, were beginning to suspect monistic pathologies like those of the eighteenth and early nineteenth centuries. Against Thomsonianism regular physicians had stressed their superior education; against homoeopaths they had to emphasize their spirit of free inquiry, their suspicion of panaceas and medical dogma. For the time being this meant losing the debate over licensing. Until they could clearly establish their superior therapy, they could not expect special treatment. But the foundation for advances in medical science was laid by their belated rejection of the search for the ultimate nature of disease. Having cast its lot against medical creeds, the profession could commit itself to careful observation of the effects of specific remedies and abandon futile descriptions of diseases in terms of vague states of bodily fluids.

The replacement of Thomsonianism by homoeopathy as the major

163

challenge to the profession was, moreover, indicative of an important change in attitude on the part of many patients. Just as the popularity of Thomsonianism in the thirties signified that many still considered a medical profession superfluous, so the rise of homoeopathy marked a growing acceptance and respect for a formally educated medical class. Unlike Thomsonians, homoeopaths never had any doubts about the need for medical schools. If they were slow to establish schools before 1860, it was for lack of funds, not enthusiasm. With the collapse of Thomsonianism, medical advisors found it increasingly difficult to gain acceptance unless they could show a command of scientific terminology. A sect which scorned medical learning had been supplanted by one which emphasized that its physicians were more learned in the science of the day than regular physicians and alone could bring to bear on medicine all the newly discovered wonders of vitality, force, and electricity.

Probably a majority of Americans continued to get their medical treatment in mild ailments from sources outside the profession. By 1860 patent medicines were serving many of the functions of domestic practitioners in colonial times. But if a sick person could not find relief through patent medicines, he was as likely as ever to seek the advice of someone presumed wise in medical matters. Before 1760 he would probably have turned to domestic practitioners; by 1860 his confidence was more likely won by someone with a semblance of formal scientific training. Regular physicians still had to prove the superiority of their therapy, but they were no longer called on to demonstrate that the sort of learning acquired in medical schools was valuable. On this point homoeopaths, Eclectics, and regular physicians were in agreement.

SIX

Conclusion:
The Ideal of Self-Regulation

VOLUNTARY ASSOCIATIONS

The medical profession greeted the repeal of penalties on unlicensed practice with a combination of relief and chagrin. Since the laws were unenforceable, they had placed a responsibility on the profession which it could not discharge. They had, in addition, excited sympathy for unlicensed practitioners, who were made to appear the victims of persecution. On the other hand, licensing had at least served as a theoretical declaration in favor of a learned profession. Repeal was also viewed, therefore, as an insult to orthodox physicians. The repeal of New York's law in 1844 had an especially telling effect. If licensing failed in that state, where the greatest number of laws had been passed, then repeal everywhere was considered inevitable. A mood of gloom settled on physicians. The profession had clearly been thrown overboard, a New York physician commented, "to sink or swim as it can, without even a rope by which to sustain itself." [1]

Disillusion with legislatures quickly grew into a broader indictment of republican institutions. An Ohio physician wrote:

> Ours is a republic of medicine, and existing as it does in the midst of a government prone to an excess of freedom, unless restrained by the strong hand of the law, or rescued by the powers of some conservative principle, within itself, its ultimate and speedy destination is alarming and most unmitigated quackery. [2]

1. E. W. Armstrong, "Address delivered before the Monroe County Medical Society . . . , May 14, 1845," *Trans., Med. Soc. State N.Y.,* 6 (1844–46), 194.
2. M. H. Houston, *An Address delivered before the Ohio County Medical Society . . . , July 5, 1847* (Wheeling, 1847), p. 3.

George Shattuck of Boston was less restrained. "We are living," he asserted,

> in an age and a community where authority is misunderstood and set at nought, where the individual feels himself called upon to treat lightly the conclusions and experience of the past, and to investigate and decide anew on most important questions and interests.[3]

Once it had been possible to describe laymen as generally sound in mind but occasionally deluded by charlatans. "Men of naturally strong minds and correct understanding," a New York physician observed in 1834, "when their intellect becomes weakened by disease and discouraged by the want of success of regular practitioners, frequently as a last resort, place themselves under the direction of these wretches [quacks], as devoid of knowledge as of moral principle."[4] As repeal took on landslide proportions, however, criticism was directed more and more at the public itself, not merely the impositions on it. In 1839 a New York physician noted a growing tendency in the public mind to patronize the ignorant and uninformed as their medical advisors. The popular mind, physicians alleged, "is radically wrong in all that relates to the healing art." The more ignorant the quack is

> of the learned lumber of the schools, or even of his own mother tongue, the more confidence is reposed in his skill, especially if he be a seventh son of the seventh daughter, or profess to have obtained his *larnin* by inspiration or immediate revelation, whether from celestial or infernal agency.

Superstition and "religious fanaticism are thus made tributary to the popular delusions, and multitudes become the victims of the stupid experimentalist on popular gullibility."[5]

Even physicians optimistic about the prospects of the profession joined in the chorus of criticism. John Francis of New York, in the

3. "The Medical Profession and Society," *Med. Communications, Mass. Med. Soc., 10* (1866) , 400.
4. A. Church, "Address delivered before the Tompkins County Medical Society in 1834," *Trans., Med. Soc. State N.Y., 4* (1838–40) , 85–86.
5. "Report of a standing committee of the Medical Society . . . , ibid., p. 228.

midst of a glowing account of the profession's position, called attention to "an obtuseness in the public mind in regard to the legitimate claims of the profession, a want of discrimination in recognizing the genuine tokens of success, and an absence of veneration for the dictates of experience." The new, the striking, "some wild fancy or chimera," were often allowed "to blind the vision of the multitude to the utility of positive knowledge."[6]

If physicians were becoming more impressed by the obtuseness of the public, the latter was cordially reciprocating. Newspapers lectured doctors on disease and even suggested that they deliberately kept their patients ill to increase their fees. A New York City daily paper denounced the profession as a "stupendous humbug." Medicine was decried for lagging behind other sciences. Popular distrust of physicians was manifested in the reluctance of legislatures to provide for vital statistics surveys or an adequate supply of subjects for dissection.[7] "The profession to which we belong," the first president of the American Medical Association declared, "has become corrupt, and degenerate, to the forfeiture of its social position, and with it, of the homage it formerly received spontaneously and universally."[8]

Some physicians confronted the situation by exalting the study of medicine over all other endeavors. "The art thus comprehended and thus practised," John Francis argued in his *Anniversary Discourse,* "can neither be overrated in its importance, nor circumscribed in its utility. In itself it is all-sufficient." The profession was not for life but a way of life. Conscious that the expectations of the founders of the American profession had not been fulfilled, physicians could not impugn the dignity of their calling and sought to reassert their influence by an expanded conception of their role. On a practical level this impetus led William Hort of Louisiana to lament the ignorance of medical graduates about soil mechanics and crop rotation and to assert that:

> All these are practical questions of great importance to
> every intelligent planter or farmer; and if the physician

6. John W. Francis, *Anniversary Discourse before the New-York Academy of Medicine* (New York, 1847), pp. 10–11, 106–07.

7. Richard H. Shryock, "Public Relations of the Medical Profession in Great Britain and the United States: 1600–1870," *Ann. Med. Hist., 2* (May 1930), 319–21.

8. "Presidential Address," *Trans. A.M.A., 1* (1848), 7.

to whom they naturally look, and to whom they apply for correct information, is unable to give it, the reflection occurs to the planter, that, after all, the doctor does not know much more than other men, notwithstanding his collegiate education, his diploma, and his high pretensions. His position as a man of scientific knowledge is necessarily forfeited, and the confidence once implicitly imposed in him is greatly impaired, if not entirely withdrawn.[9]

To defend orthodox physicians for their ability to advise on non-medical matters, however, seemed too much, and, in any event, did not solve the immediate problem presented by repeal. If there was no longer a legal distinction between practitioners, what sort of distinction could be made? It was a reasonable assumption that many people were still inclined to seek out orthodox physicians for medical treatment. Therefore some means for identifying such physicians had to be provided.

Existing medical societies could serve the purpose in some cases. The Medical and Chirurgical Faculty of Maryland, for example, continued to function, in a rather inept way, down to 1860. But most existing medical societies were not up to the task. Their opposition to Thomsonianism and internal wrangling had brought them into disrepute. Even before the repeal of licensing in New York, for example, attendance at meetings of the New York County Society had dropped off. Moreover, as long as reliance was put on official or semiofficial societies, a purge of homoeopaths could be carried out only with difficulty. An excluded homoeopath could sue for cause, and the societies, to be successful, had to prove that homoeopaths were incompetent because dogmatic. Since this charge was usually rejected in court, the simplest way to exclude them from orthodox ranks was to form new societies without licensing power.

The New York Academy of Medicine was typical of these new associations. It was formed in 1846 at the urging of Valentine Mott, president of the New York University Medical College, Alexander H. Stevens, president of the College of Physicians and Surgeons, and Isaac Wood, president of the New York County Medical Society.

9. William P. Hort, "Medical Education . . . ," *New Orleans Med. Surg. J.*, 8 (Nov. 1851), 316.

The Academy's primary purpose was the separation of regular from irregular physicians. Membership was open to regular practitioners resident in the city, state, or vicinity for three years, but proprietors and vendors of secret or patent remedies were denied admission. Lest there be any doubt about the meaning of regular medicine, it was defined as excluding:

> all homoeopathic, hydropathic, chronothermal and botanic physicians, and also all mesmeric and clairvoyant pretenders to the healing art, and all others who at any time or on any pretext claim peculiar merits for their mixed practices not founded on the best system of physiology and pathology, as taught in the best schools in Europe and America.[10]

In Ohio, medical conventions had met periodically in the twenties and early thirties. With the repeal of licensing laws the district societies and consequently the state society lost their official character. After a brief period of disorganization, medical men began to call for a new state society. Early in 1835 a convention met at Columbus. In theory, at least, its aims were ambitious—regulation of professional etiquette, construction of auxiliary societies, promotion of temperance, support for public hospitals, and the founding of a medical journal. Drake himself addressed the society in 1838 and called for a thorough reformation of the profession. He lamented the peripatetic habits of physicians, their meager education, and their endorsement of nostrums. In a spirit of self-improvement ensuing conventions passed resolutions on every conceivable aspect of professional deportment. Membership was open to individual physicians until 1846 when the convention changed its name to the Ohio State Medical Society. Thereafter membership was composed of delegates from auxiliary societies.[11]

A similar organization, the South Carolina Medical Association, held its first meeting in February 1848 and passed resolutions calling for higher educational standards and abstention from dealing with

10. Philip Van Ingen, *The New York Academy of Medicine: Its First Hundred Years* (New York, 1949), p. 13.

11. *J. Proc. Convention Physicians of Ohio* (Cincinnati, 1835), pp. 19–21; Donald D. Shira, "The Organization of the Ohio State Medical Society and Its Relation to the Ohio Medical Convention," *Ohio State Archaeol. Hist. Q.*, 50 (1941), 368–69.

druggists who sold patent medicines, whenever possible. Recognizing the problems created elsewhere by excessive local autonomy, the Association resolved at its next meeting "that the District Societies should be collateral branches of one parent Society, and that district associations with equal powers opposing each other, defeating the objects of a medical organization and bringing contempt on the whole body of the profession, should be avoided." [12] An arrangement similar to that of the Massachusetts Medical Society was adopted: district societies could make nominations, but formal approval had to come from the parent society.

The most enduring accomplishment of the movement for voluntary association, however, was the calling of a national medical convention in New York in 1846. The initiative came from delegates of the Medical Society of the State of New York, and the selection of New York University as the meeting place caused some to suspect that the convention had been called to advertise the advantages of New York City as a center for medical study. Despite these misgivings, more than 100 representatives from colleges and societies in 16 states were present at the first meeting. At the 1847 convention in Philadelphia there were 250 representatives from 21 states. The title "American Medical Association" was adopted at the third meeting in Baltimore in 1848. [13]

Physicians had long been troubled by the inferior quality of many medical schools. In 1840 Andrew Boardman celebrated his graduation from Geneva Medical College in New York with a Parthian shot at conditions there. His thesis, published as *An Essay on the Means of Improving Medical Education and Elevating Medical Character*,[14] drew a series of odious comparisons between the promises of the prospectus and fulfillment by the faculty. Boardman cited the teaching of chemistry by a Doctor of Divinity and the absence of physiology lectures as typical of conditions. The "Western Hospital," advertised as providing adequate clinical facilities, had turned out to be the second floor of a shoe store. The anatomy class had been provided with only one cadaver for the entire course. Geneva's

12. *Minutes, Proc. S.C. Med. Assoc., February, 1848–50* (Charleston, 1850), p. 42.
13. Donald E. Konold, *A History of American Medical Ethics, 1847–1912* (Madison, 1962), pp. 8–9.
14. Philadelphia, 1840.

standards were no worse than those of many rural and some urban medical schools.[15] If regular physicians were to answer the sectarian accusation that their ranks were riddled with incompetents, reforms had to be launched. The American Medical Association at once addressed itself to this necessity.

A standing committee on education was appointed at the 1846 convention and issued annual reports which were notable for their relentless castigation of American educational standards and reverential tone in describing European, and especially French, standards. Preliminary educational requirements were high in France. Therefore, the logic went, they should be raised in America. Since the term of study was longer in France, it should be lengthened from four to six months in America. The unseemly scramble for professorial chairs which had characterized the establishment of American medical schools was to be averted in the future by introduction of the French institution of the concours, or assemblage of professors from all faculties to fill a vacancy in one. The European system of direct pay of professors by the government was recommended in place of remuneration by the sale of lecture tickets.[16]

The severe penalties on unlicensed practice in all continental countries were lauded. In contrast, the "union of the business of *Teaching* and *Licensing* in the same hands" was deemed wrong in principle and "liable to great abuse in practice." Instead of the existing plethora of licensing agencies, regulation of the profession "should be restricted to one Board in each State, composed in fair proportion of representatives from its Medical Colleges and the Profession at large, and the pay for whose services as Examiners should in no degree depend on the number licensed by them." [17]

These proposals were well intentioned but there was an unmistakable air of the New Year's resolution about them. Little appreciation was shown for the distinctive aspects of either American medical education or American society. Standards were high in

15. The faculty and facilities of the medical school of New York University were persistently attacked by James Houston, an Irish immigrant who published an American *Lancet* for Bennett of the *Herald;* see Donald Fleming, *John William Draper and the Religion of Science* (Philadelphia, 1950), p. 29.

16. "Report of the Committee on Medical Education," *Trans. A.M.A.,* 2 (1849), 264–68. The 1849 report was by far the most elaborate.

17. "National Medical Convention," *New Orleans Med. Surg. J., 3* (Jan. 1848), 124.

Europe because there were very few medical schools—only three in France—and, consequently, very few physicians. The bulk of medical practice was entrusted to inferior practitioners such as apothecaries. While these individuals had often attended medical lectures, they were certainly no better qualified than the average American medical graduate.[18] American students matriculated at rural schools like that in Geneva because they could not afford to study in New York, Boston, or Philadelphia. Lengthening the term would only discourage them from attending even at Geneva. In rural America the choice was not between a graduate with a superior education and one with mediocre training but between a graduate with a semblance of education and no graduate at all.

The American Medical Association ignored another reason for the short term of study, the fact that many still considered the medical school a useful complement to apprenticeship, not the primary agency of instruction. The issue was put succinctly by the medical faculty of the University of Pennsylvania:

> Either our American system of medical education, by private preceptorship mainly, with the college and hospital as its complement, is radically wrong, or it is not. Either we should labor to perfect it, according to its idea, or we should abandon it for another.

The faculty concluded that any attempt to alter the system "will prove a ruinous patching." From the Harvard medical school came a similar rebuke, signed by Oliver Wendell Holmes, John Ware, and Jacob Bigelow, who argued that the reform agitation "proceeds from what seems to us an exaggerated view of the importance of teaching by lectures, as compared with other means of medical instruction."

The Medical College of the State of South Carolina experimented briefly with the expanded term but soon abandoned the attempt "from a conviction of its unsuitableness." The experience of the University of Buffalo was similar. Most medical schools, however, simply ignored the plea for a longer term.

The American Medical Association was no more successful in

18. For educational requirements for British apothecaries, see Charles Newman, *The Evolution of Medical Education in the Nineteenth Century* (London, 1957), p. 74.

separating teaching and licensing. A resolution to this effect, introduced at the 1846 convention, was deleted at the urging of the medical schools. To cripple the power of the latter at the national convention, a movement began in Philadelphia in 1851 to limit representation to county societies. But the voting strength of the medical schools was sufficient to defeat this proposal in 1852, 1858, and 1860.[19] The Association had once again ignored too many vested interests. While the separation of teaching and licensing would not have been disastrous for the more distinguished schools, it would have seriously damaged rural schools. For it was only by making the degree a license that the latter could interest many young men in supplementing their apprenticeship with attendance at lectures.

Intended as an agency of reform, the Association was in fact a microcosm of the profession and reflected all its weaknesses. Few of the Association's proposals bore fruit, but the fate of the concours best illustrates its failure. Of all proposals the concours stirred the most enthusiasm. Yet, after a brief trial at Rush Medical College, it had to be quickly and somewhat embarrassedly interred when it was learned that the French had abolished the concours at Paris in 1847 as too cumbersome.

The story of the other voluntary associations established after 1845 was also one of failure. The development of the South Carolina Medical Association was arrested shortly after its foundation. Although several district societies were admitted as constituent members, attendance at the annual convention dropped from 250 in 1850 to 39 in 1853. "A small attendance; failure on the part of its committees to report; the non-appearance of memoirs and essays expected and promised; a lack of interesting discussions on any scientific topic; . . . the most complete stagnation in regard to every subject of medical interest and utility" were characteristics of the Association.[20]

Problems of communication were no doubt largely responsible for professional apathy in South Carolina. But the early history of the New York Academy of Medicine was no more impressive, though most of its members lived in New York City. A difficulty had arisen

19. *Trans. A.M.A.*, 5 (1852), 25–26; 12 (1859), 49; 13 (1860), 32–33, 38.
20. Joseph I. Waring et al., *A Brief History of the South Carolina Medical Association* (Charleston, 1948), pp. 43–44.

at the Academy's inception over the exclusion of proprietors of patent and secret remedies and the prohibition on members prescribing such remedies. More than a few members gasped when Valentine Mott refused to sign the Academy's constitution because he had frequently prescribed the ether anesthetic patented by W. T. G. Morton. Orthodox physicians rarely drew the distinction between patent and secret remedies. Since the latter were protected only by copyrights on their names, their contents were never revealed. But the same objection did not apply to patent medicines. Ultimately it was decided only to prohibit fellows from giving certificates of approval to patent medicine vendors, with the provision that errant fellows were to be "reclaimed," not expelled.

Other problems were not so readily solved. The city's medical colleges had established clinics for free treatment of the poor. Since most fellows of the Academy were in private practice, they resented this competition as "unprofessional." The Academy denounced the colleges only to be rebuked by John W. Draper of New York University, who asserted that the University did not recognize the authority of the Academy of Medicine. Draper had touched a sensitive cord. Though incorporated, the Academy had no legal authority to regulate medicine. The separation of regular from irregular physicians had been quickly accomplished and abandoned as a goal. But what were regular physicians to do once they had been gathered together? The Academy now listed the advancement of science and elevation of educational standards as its objectives, but the medical schools were better equipped to achieve the former goal and the American Medical Association preempted the latter. Without a consistently defined purpose the Academy languished. Attendance was sparse; "discord was rampant and the selfish, sordid element in the Academy was more active and vociferous." [21]

The Ohio State Medical Society provided an even more notable case of failure. By 1860 it had come to resemble a preacher exhorting rows of empty pews. The state society was a federation of auxiliary societies organized on either the county or district unit—two or more counties forming a district. There were far more county than district societies, though the district societies were in a more flourishing condition. By 1860, however, only 16 of 29 auxiliary societies were

21. Van Ingen, *The New York Academy of Medicine*, pp. 14–15, 61–63.

functioning. The failure of the auxiliary societies checked any fruitful activity by the state society. On a number of occasions, for example, the state society called for new legislation to facilitate the reporting of vital statistics, but in the end it had to concede that the real problem was not the absence of laws but apathy toward existing laws. The only agencies that could gather statistics were the auxiliary societies, and their performance never came up to expectation. Even the flourishing ones rarely met more than once or twice a year. Collection of reliable statistics in such circumstances was virtually impossible.

One object long sought by the Ohio State Medical Society was the supervision of independent examinations for candidates for the medical degree. The chartering of a few unusually feeble medical colleges in various parts of the state seemed to necessitate some such regulation, but to convince either the legislature or the professors at the medical schools proved impossible. In Ohio as elsewhere there was no way to establish uniform standards for medical graduates.[22]

Frustration met the society's attempts to enforce even simple rules of medical conduct. In 1845 a series of resolutions demanding that graduates attend two full lecture courses and that members not consult with "empirics" were tabled. Had the resolutions passed, the society might have been torn apart by internal animosity since it included a fair number of Eclectic or "mixed" practitioners in its ranks. It was reluctant to expel these members, because they paid dues and supported its activities.[23] The demand that all graduates attend two full courses would have been acceptable in some states but not in Ohio. Willoughby Medical College, founded in Cleveland in 1834 and later located in Columbus, was one of the most notorious diploma mills in the country. It provided country students with a quick and cheap education. In fact it provided some of its diplomates with no education at all—a fifth of its degrees were honorary. To

22. Willoughby Medical College, technically the Medical Department of Willoughby University of Lake Erie, was started in 1834. The Medical Department of Western Reserve College commenced operations in 1843. Neither school played a role in the controversies surrounding the Medical College of Ohio. See William F. Norwood, *Medical Education in the United States before the Civil War* (Philadelphia, 1944), pp. 325–31.

23. Shira, "The Organization of the Ohio State Medical Society and Its Relation to the Ohio Medical Convention," p. 370.

require the two-course period of study would have insulted many Willoughby graduates and divided the society.[24]

The voluntary medical societies in New York, South Carolina, and Ohio sought to influence medical practice in a variety of ways. They had a dogged quality that elicits admiration despite their inglorious record. Their aims were lofty. They sought improvements of preliminary education and tighter regulation of medical ethics, especially in relation to consultations with quacks. They besought their members to write scholarly papers and to keep up with medical literature. They denounced members who advertised nostrums. In a host of ways they sought to make the profession more useful and hence more esteemed. By 1860 the voluntary associations had generally committed themselves to the ideal of the self-regulated profession.

The gap between expectation and achievement was not traceable to apathy or dilatoriness on the part of leaders. There was little joy in traveling a few hundred miles to an annual convention and then listening to the profession excoriated by its members. A strong sense of obligation was rooted in the conscience of antebellum physicians.

The problem was not moral delinquency but a fundamental flaw in the idea of voluntary association. On a theoretical level the voluntary societies were trying to move in two directions at once. One aim was professional harmony, the creation of a spirit of camaraderie that might prevent repetition of the sensational factionalism of the thirties. The corollary of this goal was a tolerant posture on the membership issue. Membership had to be encouraged if the profession was to achieve a consensus about practical objectives. No unity of purpose was possible if whole districts were not represented. But if one cause of the low state of the profession was factionalism, the other was public recognition of the lack of uniform standards among members of the profession. The only way to ensure uniform standards, however, was to follow a restrictive admissions policy. As long as the goal was professional purity, stern scrutiny had to be

24. Frederick C. Waite, "The First Medical Diploma Mill in the United States," *Bull. Hist. Med.,* 20 (Nov. 1946) , 501. John C. Bennett, founder and first president of the "University of Indiana" (sometimes called "The Christian College") became a professor at Willoughby in 1834. Bennett was convinced that the M.D. degree should be conferred after examination, regardless of the length of study. His University of Indiana was an even more celebrated diploma mill than Willoughby.

exercised in reviewing the credentials of candidates for the voluntary associations, a scrutiny few candidates could or would undergo.

The voluntary societies were thus trapped in a dilemma. Either they kept their membership requirements loose, in which case they could hardly claim to have purified their ranks, or they tightened requirements and lost any chance of presenting a united front. Time has dissipated the problem, but in 1860 there seemed no way out. If a professional society included only a quarter of the practitioners in a given state, its president could not very well say that the remaining three quarters were outside the profession. No one would have believed him, and he probably would not have believed himself.

To some extent the conflicting demands of purity and comprehensiveness had created problems before the repeal of licensing. The medical laws generally did not require licentiates to join medical societies even though the societies issued the licenses. Practice differed from state to state and within states on the membership question. Massachusetts admitted licentiates to the fellowship of its medical society after three years' practice. Elsewhere, rural societies usually encouraged membership, whereas urban societies, especially when acting as fronts for factions seeking control of local medical schools, tended to be more exclusive. But the repeal of licensing and the emergence of the homoeopathic challenge gave the issue new urgency in the late forties and fifties. As long as the main challenge was the extra-professional Thomsonianism, and as long as the societies had the official function of licensing, the medical societies could run an inconsistent course on the membership problem. Deprived of their main legal function and threatened by scientifically oriented homoeopaths, the societies had to face the issue squarely. But facing the issue meant sacrificing either purity or harmony. Unprepared to make the choice, the profession in the end accomplished neither goal.

One suspects that the constant pleas for a purer profession that emerged from annual meetings of the voluntary societies served one purpose. In a sense they provided a substitute for taking any really effective action to raise professional standards. There was virtually nothing the societies could do between 1845 and 1860 but talk about the problem. Orations at least had a cathartic effect.

The Ideal of Self-Regulation

Seeds of Stability

Physicians had been too confident of their ability to regulate practice through institutions. Their reaction to the failure of the first generation of medical societies had been to establish more societies. They would have been better advised to accept their situation and make the best of it, for there were, ironically, in the very institutions most castigated, certain stabilizing forces.

Nothing was more characteristic of American practice than that it was mainly in the hands of Doctors of Medicine. This situation did not come about without a decline in standards. Had the medical degree been as difficult to obtain as in Europe, few would have taken it. From the standpoint of regulating entrance into the profession, however, the ease with which a degree could be obtained was a blessing, since it provided a ready way of distinguishing learned from domestic practitioners. For a variety of reasons it was becoming more vital that this distinction be made.

A colonial practitioner's degree of success had been dependent on the degree of confidence he could inspire. But few could honestly claim an ability to cure certain types of disease consistently. Confidence was instead based on published or oral testimonials of occasional remarkable cures, which were often said to have been achieved through experience, a special knack, or divine inspiration. Although the physician of 1860 knew more of anatomy and physiology, his increased knowledge only made him doubtful of the value of traditional remedies. Since he could no more point to consistent and certain cures than his eighteenth-century counterpart, he also had to instill confidence in his patients in some other way.

After 1845, however, the criteria for gaining confidence began to change. The decline of Thomsonianism reflected not only the waning of Jacksonian fervor but the fading of domestic practice itself. As proprietary medical schools produced graduates en masse, there was less scope for the village clergymen and wise women of earlier days. Both the rise and collapse of Thomsonianism, moreover, were indicative of changes in patients' attitudes toward their medical advisors. Thomson himself was a transitional figure, half domestic doctor, half scientific—or pseudo-scientific—practitioner.

178

With the decline of his movement the transition was completed to the acceptance of scientific medical advisors.

That the new "science" in medicine was often pseudo-science cannot be too strongly emphasized. The same intellectual atmosphere that produced homoeopathy and the mesmeric fad of the forties was to give rise to spiritualism and Christian Science, as the emphasis of mind over matter delicately established by the homoeopaths was upset in later years by an outright denial of matter. But pseudo-science is often the matrix of science. Pseudo-science, in other words, is an attempt to seek too many scientific laws too quickly—not sub-science but super-science.

Pseudo-science in the form of homoeopathy, phrenology, or mesmerism (as the latter was practiced in the forties) was based on a relentless and overzealous endeavor to seek laws behind the universe. But in the process homoeopaths did much to popularize and owed much of their success to the growing acceptance of the notion that there could be a consistent theory leading to certain cures which could be comprehended only after years of study.

The terms of the debate between regular and irregular physicians had thus been redefined. In the eighteenth and early nineteenth centuries the full-time physician with formal training had sought to establish his superiority over the part-time empirical practitioner. But by 1850 the debate was between two types of full-time educated physicians.

The redefinition of terms was favorable to orthodox medicine. Homoeopaths and Eclectics were popular in many places, but they were far fewer in number than domestic practitioners in the eighteenth century or Thomsonians in the 1830s. A reasonable estimate would be one sectarian for every ten orthodox physicians in 1860 (see Appendix 2). In 1760 there certainly had been no more than one regular physician for every ten domestic practitioners. The repeal of penalties on unlicensed practice, instead of causing an avalanche of quackery, had almost the opposite effect. By depriving Thomsonians of their cherished cry of persecution, it lessened their popularity and hastened their decline. Eclectics and homoeopaths were thus left alone in their confrontation of orthodox medicine.

Medical institutions either did not serve their original purpose or they accomplished results almost by accident. Medical societies, designed to distinguish regular from empirical practitioners and extinguish the latter, came to grief. Medical schools, designed to raise professional standards, multiplied so rapidly that they frustrated this object and, in addition, damaged the position of the medical societies. But precisely because there were so many schools, the medical degree in effect accomplished the separation of regular from empirical practitioners. At the same time a subtle change in popular attitudes which produced a demand for medical advisors versed in scientific terminology brought about a tightening of requirements for entering the profession where innumerable laws and organizations had failed. The medical profession on the eve of the Civil War was thus better regulated than it had been at any other time in American history, not because of institutions but in spite of them.

APPENDIX ONE

Summary of Licensing Legislation

NEW YORK

1760
1. Applied to N.Y.C.
2. No one to practice until examined by officials in consultation with physicians.
3. Fines imposed for noncompliance.

1792
1. Applied to N.Y.C.
2. Required 2 to 3 years' apprenticeship before examination.
3. Did not affect practicing physicians or holders of M.D.
4. Prohibition on suing for fees in cases of noncompliance.

1797
1. Applied to whole state.
2. Candidates for license must produce testimonials of 4 years' study.
3. But 2 years' study or practice sufficient for those already in practice.
4. Fines for noncompliance.

1806
1. Provided for incorporation of county medical societies.
2. Censors of county societies could grant licenses if candidates presented testimonials of 3 years' study and passed their examination.
3. Prohibition on suing for fees.

1807
1. Fine of $5 per month on unlicensed doctors.
2. Exemption for those who used domestic roots and herbs.

1809
1. M.D. granted by regents recognized as license.

1812
1. Penalty raised to $25 for each offense.

1813
1. Compilation of unrepealed parts of preceding laws.
2. $10 fee for license of a county society.
3. Emphasizes role of state society as court of appeals for rejected candidates.

1818
1. Term of study prior to examination fixed at 4 years, though one could be deducted if candidate

181

1818 (cont.)

had attended one full course of medical lectures.

2. State society allowed to elect censors.

3. Medical colleges given representation at state society.

1819

1. No medical school to grant degree until student had attended one full course of all lectures in the school.

1827

1. Provisions made for serving notice on unlicensed practitioners that they must conform to law.

2. Procedures outlined for barring from practice members of county societies convicted of gross ignorance or misconduct.

3. No appeal allowed from one county society to another.

4. No person coming from another state or county could practice until he filed his diploma with clerk of county where he resided, and exhibited satisfactory evidence of study.

5. No person could receive M.D. from regents till proof given he had studied for 3 years under a regular physician and attended two complete courses in an incorporated medical school, provided the last course be taken in the school granting the M.D.

6. M.D. granted by medical schools in the state no longer a license. M.D. granted by regents still a license.

7. No medical school to institute a faculty except where charter locates the school.

8. Unlicensed practice a misdemeanor subject to fine and imprisonment. Botanic exemption removed.

9. Other provisions of 1806–19 laws not altered or repealed by this law deemed still in force.

1830

1. Botanic doctors exempted from all penalties.

1834

1. Botanic doctors cannot sue for fees.

1835

1. 1834 law repealed.

2. M.D. granted by Geneva College made a license.

1836

1. Practitioners coming from other states or nations to be re-examined by state medical society.

1844

1. All laws prohibiting any persons from suing for fees repealed.

2. No person liable to criminal prosecution for practicing medicine without a license unless convicted of gross ignorance, malpractice, or immoral conduct.

1853

1. M.D. to be granted in future by trustees of medical schools.

2. Medical schools to be chartered directly by regents.

MASSACHUSETTS

1781

1. Mass. Medical Society incorporated with licensing power.
2. Number of fellows limited to 70.
3. No penalties on unlicensed practitioners.

1803

1. Licentiates could become fellows after 3 years' practice.
2. Harvard M.D.'s admitted as licentiates without examination.
3. District societies could be formed on the application of any five fellows.

1806 bylaw

1. Consultation with unlicensed practitioners forbidden.

1818

1. No person can sue for fees till licensed by Mass. Med. Soc. or granted M.D. by an incorporated college.

1819

1. No person to sue for fees till licensed by Mass. Med. Soc. or granted M.D. by Harvard.
2. Those licensed by out-of-state authority to be examined by Mass. Med. Soc.

1831

1. Graduates of Harvard with M.D. admitted to Mass. Med. Soc. immediately as fellows.

1834

1. Bodies of paupers made available to licensed physicians for dissection.

1835

1. Unlicensed practitioners no longer barred from suing for fees.

1837

1. Graduates of Berkshire Medical Institution given same privileges as Harvard graduates.

1837 bylaw

1. Medical graduates of Harvard and Berkshire must join the Mass. Med Soc. within one year after graduation.

1840

1. 1837 bylaw repealed. Graduates of Harvard and Berkshire not required to join but can be admitted without examination.

1856

1. Homoeopathic Medical Society incorporated.

1859

1. Privileges of Harvard and Berkshire graduates removed.
2. Omission of mention of Mass. Med. Soc. from Revised Statutes.

1860

1. No sectarian physician to be admitted to the Mass. Med. Soc.

MARYLAND

1799

1. Medical and Chirurgical Faculty incorporated and authorized to elect a Medical Board of Examiners.
2. Unlicensed practitioners subject to fine and forbidden to sue for fees.

1838
1. 1799 law's prohibition on suing for fees removed.

SOUTH CAROLINA

1817
1. Licensing boards established at Charleston and Columbia. Medical Society of South Carolina to act as Charleston board.
2. Penalties of fine, imprisonment, and prohibition on suing for fees.

1828
1. No one to be licensed until he has diploma from some medical institution or passes an examination by faculty of Medical College of South Carolina.
2. The above are preliminaries to examination by license boards.

1838
1. Fine and imprisonment penalties repealed.

1845
1. Prohibition on suing repealed.

OHIO

1811
1. State divided into five medical districts.
2. Three censors in each district appointed by the assembly and encharged with examining candidates.

1812
1. Medical Society of the State of Ohio created.
2. Law designates 120 members.
3. State divided into seven medical districts.

4. Physicians in each district to form a medical society.
5. Each district society can send two or three members to state medical convention.
6. State medical society to appoint censors.
7. Unlicensed practitioners forbidden to sue for fees and made subject to fines.
8. Medical societies forbidden to fix prices.

1813
1. General assembly named censors in each district.

1817
1. District societies can appoint censors.

1818
1. Doctors of Medicine licensed without examination.

1821
1. Nine medical districts designated with five censors named in each district.
2. Medical Convention of Ohio created, composed of one delegate from each district.
3. Examinations placed in hands of Medical Convention of Ohio.

1821–33
1. Various laws increasing number of medical districts.

1833
1. Repeal of penalties on unlicensed practice.
2. Repeal of all laws incorporating medical societies.

APPENDIX TWO

Irregular Practitioners
in the United States

The figure of one sectarian for every ten orthodox physicians is intended as no more than a rough but reasonable estimate. It is based on three contemporary surveys and one made by the author.

In 1858 a New York physician estimated that there were 31,000 regular physicians, 1,000 homoeopaths, 400 hydropaths, 800 Eclectics, 600 botanics (Physio-Medicals), and 300 female physicians (mainly botanic) in the United States. Adding a large number of itinerant nostrum vendors, the number came to 3,000 to 4,000 irregular physicians, or a proportion of one irregular practitioner to ten regular practitioners.[1] These figures were allegedly based on a questionnaire sent to all states, but it was conceded that comparative estimates were made where no returns were received. One suspects that many such comparative estimates were made, but the figures serve as a useful guide.

In 1852 the South Carolina Medical Association surveyed practice in the state. No accurate returns were received from seven counties, but the returns from the remaining twenty counties were described as highly accurate. There were 700 practitioners in these twenty districts. Of these, 660 were either graduates of orthodox medical colleges or licentiates of the Medical Society of South Carolina. The remainder were divided about equally between "irregular" practitioners (Eclectics, Physio-Medicals, and a few homoeopaths) and "unauthorized" practitioners (Indian doctors, natural bonesetters, and cancer doctors).[2] The number of "unauthorized" practitioners had probably remained constant since 1830. But observers noted that there were far fewer sectarian physicians in South Carolina after 1845. The collapse of Thomsonianism was complete and homoeopathy was never a significant force in the state. These factors account for the state's relatively low percentage of irregular and unauthorized practitioners.

1. Dan King, *Quackery Unmasked* (New York, ca. 1858), pp. 332–33.
2. *Proc. S.C. Med. Assoc., 1852* (Charleston, 1852), p. 9.

The *Massachusetts Register* of 1858 printed statistics on regular, homoeopathic, and botanic physicians in the state. According to the *Register,* there were 1,400 regular physicians, 35 homoeopaths, and 108 botanics in practice in 1857. The proportion of sectarian to regular physicians was thus about one to ten. The figure of 35 homoeopaths was probably too low. According to the standard history of American homoeopathy, 142 homoeopaths began practice in Massachusetts between 1845 and 1857, and it is likely that more than 35 were still in practice in the latter year. But granting this, the figure would still be close to one sectarian for ten orthodox physicians.

Approximately 2,400 homoeopaths practiced in the United States at one time or another between 1835 and 1860, the great majority after 1845.[3] Adding a guess about Eclectic and Physio-Medical strength, there were perhaps 7,000 sectarian practitioners in the 1845–60 period. In the same period there were some 20,000 orthodox medical graduates and about 40,000 orthodox matriculants who never bothered to take degrees.[4] This would give a proportion of one sectarian to 8.50 orthodox physicians.

3. Calculated by myself from King, *History of Homoeopathy, 1,* passim.

4. See *Boston Med. Surg. J., 36* (May 5, 1847) , 280. The *Journal* estimated that there were 4,500 medical students and 1,300 graduates in 1847. Since the degree course lasted two years, 1,900 students never took degrees (i.e., 4,500 minus 2,600) . It should be added that this is simply an estimate by a generally observant periodical.

CRITICAL ESSAY ON SOURCES

There is no comprehensive history of the medical profession in America. Henry Burnell Shafer's *The American Medical Profession, 1783 to 1850* is somewhat dated but a useful starting point. Richard H. Shryock's *Medicine and Society in America, 1660–1860* is more interpretive than comprehensive but represents an outstanding synthesis of a wide range of materials and suggests numerous possibilities for further study. More specific studies are listed below in the order in which the topics they treat appear in the text.

ENGLISH BACKGROUND

There are many useful works on specific centuries or institutions, such as W. S. C. Copeman's *Doctors and Disease in Tudor Times* and Zachary Cope's *The Royal College of Surgeons of England: A History*. These writers tend to view the whole picture of English medical practice through the eyes of London physicians and surgeons (both Cope and Copeman are fellows of the royal colleges). This leads them to slight the importance of provincial developments and overestimate the role played by the royal colleges. R. S. Roberts, a professional historian, offers a useful corrective to this bias in two articles on "The Personnel and Practice of Medicine in Tudor and Stuart England." The best summary of English medical legislation is by J. W. Willcock—*The Laws Relating to the Medical Profession*.

COLONIAL PERIOD

Francis Packard has fulfilled the task which he set for himself in his *History of Medicine in the United States,* "to collect as many facts as possible" about colonial medicine. But his work is poorly organized and often inaccurate. By far the best studies of colonial medicine are Wyndham Blanton's two volumes, *Medicine in Virginia in the Seventeenth Century* and *Medicine in Virginia in the Eighteenth Century*. Blanton has rendered an invaluable service in gleaning facts relevant to the pro-

187

fession from county archives, thus enabling us to reconstruct the daily lives of colonial practitioners.

Other colonies have not been so well served. Henry Viets' *A Brief History of Medicine in Massachusetts* adds little to Oliver Wendell Holmes' delightful but thin "The Medical Profession in Massachusetts." There is some valuable information on the colonial period in the first volume of James J. Walsh's five-volume *History of Medicine in New York*. Until Joseph I. Waring recently published *A History of Medicine in South Carolina, 1670–1825,* David Ramsey's eighty-page sketch in the second volume of his *History of South Carolina* was the best treatise on medicine in that colony.

Few colonial physicians have been the subjects of adequate biographies. The best on the seventeenth and early eighteenth centuries is that of Otho Beall, Jr., and Richard H. Shryock, *Cotton Mather: First Significant Figure in American Medicine.* John Brett Langstaff's *Doctor Bard of Hyde Park* is valuable for the mid-eighteenth century.

Whitfield Bell has synthesized a wide range of material in "Medical Practice in Colonial America." Chapters 34–37 of Daniel Boorstin's *The Americans: The Colonial Experience* present a provocative interpretation of colonial practice.

MASSACHUSETTS

Walter Burrage's *History of the Massachusetts Medical Society* is the best reference work, but it is narrow in scope and in places becomes simply a recounting of bylaws. The *Medical Communications and Dissertations of the Massachusetts Medical Society* (various titles, see below) were published periodically and contain an abundance of scientific and professional information. The same applies to the weekly *Boston Medical and Surgical Journal,* whose issues between 1828 and 1860 were systematically examined. I have studied the Records of the Massachusetts Medical Society in the society's library in Boston, but this source did not alter the picture received from the published transactions of the society. Reginald Fitz's *Rise and Fall of the Licensed Physician in Massachusetts* is the best survey of licensing legislation but is inaccurate in places.

The statutes relating to the society are scattered through a number of collections of Commonwealth laws, but these were periodically published by the society in digests. Massachusetts House and Senate *Documents* generally contain only drafts of bills, not committee reports or reports of debates, and were not nearly so helpful as similar documents in New York.

Critical Essay on Sources

The Harvard College Library contains a wealth of manuscript material relating to the Waterhouse controversy. This includes apologies written by Waterhouse, replies by Warren, and counter-replies by Waterhouse. I have traced the issues involved in the Harvard College Records from 1785 to 1810. Waterhouse took up the cudgels in the *New England Palladium* throughout 1811 and was assailed in its pages by Warren.

NEW YORK

Charles B. Coventry's "History of Medical Legislation in the State of New York" provides a useful introduction to licensing laws but must be used with care for the period 1830–1844. The medical laws of the state are accessible in the *Laws of the State of New York*. The *Journals* and *Documents* of the New York House and Senate contain committee reports and floor debates about medical laws and were more helpful than public documents in any other state.

There is an excellent discussion of some aspects of the New York profession in Daniel Calhoun's *Professional Lives in America*. The second volume of James J. Walsh's five-volume *History of Medicine in New York* contains abundant information about the College of Physicians and Surgeons schism but must be supplemented by William F. Norwood's *Medical Education in the United States before the Civil War*, chapter 10. David Hosack's *Inaugural Address Delivered before the Rutgers Medical College* contains a mass of documents and a distinct bias. To obtain the county society's side of the story I have consulted the Minutes of the Medical Society of the County of New York, 1806–1850, which are kept in the New York Academy of Medicine.

The *Transactions of the Medical Society of the State of New York* have proved extremely valuable. They contain reprints of speeches on quackery and the state of the profession, local medical news, and abstracts of legislative committee reports. The activities of the county medical societies outside of New York City are known only through their appearance in the *Transactions*.

I have used two New York newspapers extensively; the *New York Whig* on Kappa Lambda, and the *Albany Argus* to determine the party affiliation of senators and assemblymen voting to repeal licensing.

SOUTH CAROLINA

The Minutes of the Medical Society of South Carolina, 1789–1850, in the library of the Medical College of South Carolina, are the best single source for the profession's history in the period. Joseph I. Waring has published well-chosen *Excerpts* from the minutes. The "unhappy schism" produced a number of pamphlets. Most important are *An Exposition of the Affairs of the Medical Society of South Carolina,* Dickson's *Statements in Reply,* and T. Y. Simons' *A Reply to a Pamphlet by Henry Dickson, M.D.* Since each party was concerned to justify its past actions to the public, the pamphlets contain voluminous reprints of charters and legal decisions. There is a treatment of the schism in Norwood's *Medical Education in the United States before the Civil War,* chapter 22.

The *Charleston Medical Journal* did not begin publication until after the schism, but the volumes covering 1846 to 1854 were useful for biographical sketches of participants in the schism. South Carolina public documents were not very helpful. There are no House and Senate *Documents* as in New York, and the *Journals* of those bodies contained little in the way of debate over licensing. The laws themselves are in the *South Carolina Statutes at Large.* I have examined a number of newspapers and made use of the *Charleston Mecury* to some extent.

MARYLAND

Maryland public documents were generally more useful than those of Massachusetts, less valuable than similar sources in New York. For reports of legislative debates before 1830 the historian must take his chances with newspaper accounts. After that date the *Journals* of the House and Senate are useful. The main pieces of legislation relating to the university are scattered through the *Laws of Maryland.*

The early records of the Medical and Chirurgical Faculty yield only the most fragmentary information concerning its activities. The best account of the contest for control of the university is contained in Nathaniel Potter's *Some Account of the Rise and Progress of the University of Maryland.* Potter's biases are massive but, fortunately, fairly obvious to the reader. Many of the particulars of the issue between regents and trustees are reprinted in *Regents of the University of Maryland v. Joseph B. Williams.*

George Callcott's *A History of the University of Maryland* is balanced and judicious on the trustees–regents struggle. Eugene F. Cordell's *Medical Annals of Maryland* and *Historical Sketch of the University of Maryland* contain vast quantities of data on the early history of the University of Maryland and on the Maryland profession. There is a splendid biographical file covering a huge number of prominent Maryland citizens in the Baltimore Public Library. This was helpful in tracking down some of the participants in the regents–trustees controversy.

OHIO

Emmet F. Horine's excellent biography of Daniel Drake has replaced Otto Juettner's *Daniel Drake and His Followers* as the best study on the Cincinnati profession in the antebellum period. The *Ohio State Archaeological and Historical Quarterly* long had a special section devoted to Ohio medical history. Cincinnati physicians were notoriously prone to publicizing their grievances, a fact which makes the Cincinnati newspapers an invaluable source. The best collection of newspapers is owned by the Cincinnati Historical Society. Polemical pamphlets like Drake's *Rise and Fall* and Henry's *An Exposure* have to be used with caution but are still useful. The Cincinnati Historical Society has rich and well-catalogued manuscript collections, including the Lytle Papers which contain considerable information relevant to political alignments within the medical profession. The library of the University of Cincinnati Medical School also contains some rare material on Drake. Ohio public documents are moderately useful, especially the House *Journal* for the 1833–1835 period. The *Transactions* of the Ohio State Medical Society are less informative than those of the New York and Massachusetts state societies.

UPPER CANADA

Little has been written about Canadian medical history. William Canniff's *The Medical Profession in Upper Canada, 1783–1850* is essentially a running commentary on source material. It is informative but dull and badly organized. The same is true of Heagerty's *Four Centuries of Medical History in Canada*. The *Historical Bulletin* of the Calgary Associate Clinic contains a number of articles on Canadian medical history but they are of uneven quality and accuracy. Some material can be found in university histories like D. D. Calvin's *Queen's University at Kingston, 1841–1941*.

THOMSONIANISM

There are several secondary studies of Thomsonianism, including a chapter in James Harvey Young's *Toadstool Millionaires*, Philip D. Jordan's "The Secret Six, An Inquiry into the Basic Materia Medica of the Thomsonian System of Botanic Medicine," and Alex Berman's Ph.D. dissertation, "The Impact of the Nineteenth Century Botanico-Medical Movement on American Medicine and Pharmacy." Berman has also written two articles on the subject: "Neo-Thomsonianism in the United

191

States," and "A Striving for Scientific Respectability: Some American Botanics and the Nineteenth Century Plant Materia Medica." But for present purposes all these works have been found unsatisfactory. Young is preoccupied with the role of Thomsonianism in the history of patent-medicine law; Jordan and Berman primarily with the influence of the botanic movement on pharmacy. For my purpose I have found the botanic journals themselves most helpful. Many of these journals led a shadowy existence. Even the most widely circulated did not survive for long, and no library has a complete file. I have concentrated on the *Thomsonian Messenger, Thomsonian Botanic Watchman, Boston Thomsonian Manual,* and Alva Curtis' *Botanico-Medical Recorder* (which became the chief neo-Thomsonian organ). In addition, I have made extensive use of Samuel Thomson's *New Guide to Health and Narrative.* These works, sometimes published together, went through a number of editions, with occasional additions of material. I have used the second edition (Boston, 1825), the fourth (Columbus, 1827), and the Boston edition of 1835 (no edition number given). Four libraries were especially helpful for obtaining copies of the journals and the *New Guide* and *Narrative:* the library of the Harvard Medical School, the Boston Medical Library, the New York Academy of Medicine's library, and the library of the Medical College of South Carolina. For understanding the mentality of a typical (in the strict sense) Thomsonian one can do no better than read Elias Smith's autobiography. Alexander Wilder's *History of Medicine* contains abundant (but undocumented) information about the history of the botanic movement. It is propagandistic in tone, however, and must be used with caution.

HOMOEOPATHY

I have used the third American edition of Hahnemann's *Organon* which, in addition to being the most accessible, was the edition used by most American homoeopaths.

The early American homoeopaths wrote scores of apologetic pamphlets for their system. The best ones are Alexis Eustaphieve's *Homoeopathia Revealed* and Edward Bayard's *Homoeopathia and Nature and Allopathia and Art.* The *Homoeopathic Examiner* was studied for the periods 1840–43 and 1845–47, but this did not alter the picture received from the pamphlets. Oliver Wendell Holmes' "Homoeopathy and Its Kindred Delusions" remains one of the best demolition jobs in American polemical literature. Worthington Hooker's *Physician and Patient* and *The Present Attitude and Tendencies of the Medical Profession* are perceptive studies of the influence of sectarianism on the profession.

Critical Essay on Sources

Unlike Thomsonians, homoeopaths survived into the twentieth century and have written about the early history of the movement. Especially valuable is the first volume of William King's four-volume edition of the *History of Homoeopathy and Its Institutions in America*. Thomas L. Bradford's *Homoeopathic Bibliography of the United States* was of great assistance, since it includes the nonmedical as well as medical writings of American Homoeopaths.

BIBLIOGRAPHY

PRIMARY SOURCES

MANUSCRIPTS

Diary of Major Daniel Gano. Cincinnati Historical Society.

Gano Papers. Cincinnati Historical Society.

Harvard College Records, vols. *3* and *4* covering 1778–1810. Harvard College Library.

Lytle Family Papers; Lytle Papers. Cincinnati Historical Society.

Minutes of the Medical Society of South Carolina, 1789–1850. Library of the Medical College of South Carolina.

Minutes of the Medical Society of the County of New York, 1806–50. Rare Book Room of the New York Academy of Medicine.

Papers relating to the Waterhouse Controversy, 1812. Harvard College Library.

Records of the Massachusetts Medical Society, 1785–1860. Society's library in Boston.

Reply of the Harvard Faculty to Waterhouse, a letter to the Revd. and Hon. the Pres. and Fellows, Feb. 27, 1812. Harvard College Library.

Waterhouse, Benjamin, Apology to the Corporation for Novum Organon. Harvard College Library.

PERIODICALS AND TRANSACTIONS.

Boston Medical and Surgical Journal, 1828–60. Vols. *1–62*.

Boston Thomsonian Manual, 1835–41. Vols. *1–7*. Vols. 1838–41 entitled *Boston Thomsonian Manual and Lady's Companion*.

Boston True Thomsonian, 1840–43. Vols. *1–3*.

Botanico-Medical Recorder (Cincinnati), 1838, 1844–45. Vols. *6, 12, 13*.

Buchanan's Journal of Man (Cincinnati; 1849–50), 1849, vol. *1*.

Charleston Medical Journal. 1846–54. Vols. *1–9*.

Homoeopathic Examiner (N.Y.C.), 1840–43, 1845–47. Vols. *1–3* and n.s. *1, 2*.

Journal of the Proceedings of a Convention of Physicians of Ohio. Cincinnati, 1835.

Journal of the Proceedings of the Medical Convention of Ohio . . . second session . . . 1838. Cincinnati, 1838.

Journal of Proceedings of the Medical Convention of Ohio at its Third Session, 1839. Cleveland, 1839.

Bibliography

L'Homoion: Journal de la Société Hahnemanniane de la Nouvelle-Orléans, 1860–61. Vols. *1, 2.*

Medical Communications of the Massachusetts Medical Society, 1. Boston, 1808.

Medical Communications and Dissertations of the Massachusetts Medical Society, 2. Boston, 1813.

Medical Dissertations delivered at the Annual Meetings of the Massachusetts Medical Society, 3. Boston, 1822.

Medical Dissertations of the Massachusetts Medical Society and other Medical Papers, 4. Boston, 1829. Contains an appendix with proceedings of the councillors covering 1822–29.

Medical Communications of the Massachusetts Medical Society, 5. Boston, 1836. With an appendix covering proceedings of the councillors, 1830–36.

Medical Communications of the Massachusetts Medical Society, with an Appendix containing Proceedings of the Society, 6. Boston, 1841. Proceedings cover 1842–48.

Medical Communications of the Massachusetts Medical Society with an Appenddix containing Proceedings of the Society, 7. Boston, 1854. Proceedings cover 1849–54.

Medical Communications of the Massachusetts Medical Society with an Appendix containing Proceedings of the Society, 8. Boston, 1854. Proceedings cover 1849–54.

Medical Communications of the Massachusetts Medical Society with an Appendix containing Proceedings of the Councillors of the Society, 9. Boston, 1860. Proceedings cover 1855–60.

Minutes of the Ohio State Medical Society, . . . 1851. Columbus, 1851.

Minutes of the Ohio State Medical Society, . . . 1852. Cleveland, 1853.

New Orleans Medical and Surgical Journal, 1844–60. Vols. *1–12.* First two volumes entitled *New Orleans Medical Journal.*

Le Practicien Homéopathe: Journal de Médecine Homéopathique (New Orleans), Nov. 1857–Oct. 1858 (only issues published).

Proceedings of the National Medical Conventions Held in New York, May 1846, and in Philadelphia, May 1847. Philadelphia, 1847.

Proceedings of the Ohio Medical Convention held at Columbus, 1847. Columbus, 1847.

Proceedings of the South Carolina Medical Association, sessional, 1849–53, Charleston, 1849–53.

Southern Botanic Journal (Charleston), Feb. 1837–Dec. 1838. Vols. *1, 2.*

Thomsonian Botanic Watchman (Albany, N.Y.), Jan.–Dec. 1834. Vol. *1.*

Thomsonian Messenger (Norwich, Conn.), July 1841–June 1843. Vols. *1, 2.*

Transactions of the American Medical Association, 1848–60, sessional, Philadelphia, 1848–60.

Transactions of the Medical Society of the State of New York From Its Organization in 1807, up to and including 1831. Albany, 1868.

Transactions of the Medical Society of the State of New York, 1832–46. 6 vols. Vol. *1* covers 1832–33; *2,* 1834–35; *3,* 1836–37; *4,* 1838–40; *5,* 1840–43; *6,* 1844–

46. Albany, 1833, 1835, 1837, 1868, 1848; first edition not extant for vol. *5*, which was republished in 1868.

Transactions of the 9th Annual Meeting of the Ohio State Medical Society, . . . 1854. Cincinnati, 1854.

Transactions of the 14th Annual Meeting of the Ohio State Medical Society, . . . 1859. Columbus, 1859.

Transactions of the 15th Annual Meeting of the Ohio State Medical Society, . . . 1860. Columbus, 1860.

Western Journal of the Medical and Physical Sciences (Cincinnati), 1829–35. Vols. *3–8.*

BOOKS, PAMPHLETS, AND ARTICLES

Abernethy, John, "An Enquiry into the Probability and Rationality of Mr. Hunter's Theory of Life," *Introductory Lectures, Exhibiting some of Mr. Hunter's Opinions Respecting Life and Diseases, delivered before the Royal College of Surgeons, London, in 1814 and 1815.* London, 1823.

Address of the Trustees of the University of Maryland to the Public. Baltimore, 1830.

[Atkinson, William], "The Water Cure," *Christian Examiner,* 4 ser., *10* (July 1848), 33–48.

Bartlett, Elisha, *An Inquiry into the Degree of Certainty in Medicine; and into the Nature and Extent of its Powers over Disease.* Philadelphia, 1848.

Bayard, Edward, *Homoeopathia and Nature and Allopathia and Art.* New York, 1858.

Beach, Wooster, *The American Practice of Medicine; Being a Treatise on the Character, Causes, Symptoms, Morbid Appearances and Treatment of the Diseases of Men, Women, and Children . . . As Taught at the Reformed Medical Colleges in the United States: Containing also a Treatise on Materia Medica and Pharmacy.* 3 vols. New York, 1833.

Bellinger, John, *A History of "the Stamp Act" of the Medical Society of South-Carolina.* Charleston, 1835.

Biegler, Augustus, *A Discourse on Allopathia and Homoeopathia.* Rochester, 1843.

Bigelow, Jacob, "On Self-Limited Diseases," *Medical Communications of the Massachusetts Medical Society, 5* (1830–36), 319–58.

Boardman, Andrew, *An Essay on the Means of Improving Medical Education and Elevating Medical Character.* Philadelphia, 1840.

[Bonsall, Joseph], *Controversy in Relation to the Medical Schools of Ohio and Commercial Hospital and Lunatic Asylum.* Cincinnati, 1839.

Buchanan, Joseph Rodes, *Sketches of Buchanan's Discoveries in Neurology.* Louisville, 1842.

Bush, George, *Mesmer and Swedenborg; or the Relation of the Development of Mesmerism to the Doctrines and Disclosures of Swedenborg.* New York, 1847.

Caustic, Christopher. See Fessenden, Thomas G.

Bibliography

Channing, Walter, "Of the Medical Profession and its Preparation," *Boston Medical and Surgical Journal, 33* (Nov. 19, 1845), 309–37.

Church, A., "Address delivered before the Tompkins County Medical Society in 1834," *Transactions of the Medical Society of the State of New York, 4* (1838–40), 85–93.

A Circular Letter to the Practitioners of Physic and Surgery in the State of New-York from the Practitioners of Physic and Surgery in the County and City of New-York with a Memorial intended to be submitted to the Legislature of the State of New-York at the next session. New York, 1829.

De Charms, Richard, *A Defense of Homoeopathy against Her New-Church Assailants.* Philadelphia, 1854.

Dickson, Samuel H., *Statements in Reply to Certain Publications from the Medical Society of South Carolina.* Charleston, 1834.

Drake, Daniel, *A Narrative of the Rise and Fall of the Medical College of Ohio.* Cincinnati, 1822.

———, "The People's Doctors," *Western Journal of the Medical and Physical Sciences, 3* (Oct.–Dec. 1829), 395–408.

———, *Practical Essays on Medical Education and the Medical Profession in the United States.* Cincinnati, 1832.

"Duties of Physicians," *Boston Medical and Surgical Journal, 36* (June 9, 1847), 378–82.

"The Duty of Medical Men with respect to Homoeopathy," *Boston Medical and Surgical Journal, 42* (Feb. 27, 1850), 73–77.

Epps, John, *Homoeopathy and its Principles Revealed.* London, 1850.

Eustaphieve, Alexis, *Homoeopathia Revealed.* New York, 1846.

Eve, Paul, *The Present Position of the Medical Profession in Society.* Augusta, Ga., 1849.

An Exposition of the Affairs of the Medical College of South-Carolina so far as They Appertain to the Establishment of a Medical College in Charleston, and the subsequent Division of the Latter. Charleston, 1833.

Fessenden, Thomas G. (Christopher Caustic, pseud.), *The Modern Philosopher; or Terrible Tractoration!* 2d Amer. ed. Philadelphia, 1806.

Forbes, John, *Of Nature and Art in the Cure of Disease.* 1st Amer. ed. New York, 1858.

Francis, John W., *Anniversary Discourse before the New-York Academy of Medicine.* New York, 1847.

Gould, Augustus A., "Search out the Secrets of Nature," *Medical Communications of the Massachusetts Medical Society, 9* (1855–60), 1–45.

Green, Joseph H., *Vital Dynamics: The Hunterian Oration before the Royal College of Surgeons in London, 14th February, 1840.* London, 1840.

Gregory, Samuel, *Letters to Ladies in favor of Female Physicians for Their Own Sex.* Boston, 1856.

Hahnemann, Samuel, *Organon der Heilkunst.* 2d. ed. Leipsig, 1827.

———, *Organon of the Homoeopathic Art.* Trans. with an introduction by Constantine Hering. 3d. Amer. ed. New York, 1849.

Bibliography

Hempel, Charles J., *The True Organization of the New Church as indicated in the writings of Emanuel Swedenborg, and as demonstrated by Charles Fourier.* New York, 1848.

Henry, John F., *An Exposure of the Conduct of the Trustees and Professors of the Medical College of Ohio, and of the Hospital and Township Trustees.* Cincinnati, 1833.

Holcombe, William H., *How I Became a Homoeopath.* Chicago, 1866.

———, *The Other Life.* Philadelphia, 1871.

———, *Scientific Basis of Homoeopathy.* Cincinnati, 1852.

Hooker, Worthington, *Dissertation on the Respect due to the Medical Profession and the Reasons that it is not awarded by the Community.* Norwich, Conn., 1844.

———, *Physician and Patient; or a Practical View of the Mutual Duties, Relations and Interests of the Medical Profession and the Community.* New York, 1849.

———, *The Present Attitude and Tendencies of the Medical Profession.* New Haven, 1852.

———, "Rational Therapeutics," *Publications of the Massachusetts Medical Society, 1* (1860), 151–218.

Hosack, David, *An Inaugural Address delivered before the Rutgers Medical College.* New York, 1826.

Houston, M. H., *An Address delivered before the Ohio County Medical Society on the Evening of its Organization, July 5, 1847.* Wheeling, 1847.

[Jarvis, Edward], "Law of Physical Life," *Christian Examiner,* 3 ser., *17* (Sept. 1843), 1–31.

Lawrence, William, *Lectures on Psychology, Zoology, and the Natural History of Man, delivered at the Royal College of Surgeons.* London, 1822.

Leland, P. W., "Empiricism and its Causes," *Boston Medical and Surgical Journal, 47* (Nov. 3, 1852), 283–94.

Medical Department of Cincinnati College to the Public. Cincinnati, 1835.

"Medical Education in the United States," *Boston Medical and Surgical Journal, 29* (Nov. 29, 1843), 329–33.

Morley, Charles, *Elements of Animal Magnetism.* New York, ca. 1845.

Nardin, Daniel F., *An Address to the People of South Carolina Shewing the Unconstitutionality, Injustice and Impolicy of the Medical Law of the State.* Charleston, 1835.

Peabody, Elizabeth Palmer, *Memorial to Dr. William Wesselhoeft, to which is added his last address to the homoeopathic association.* Boston, 1859.

"The Pecuniary Condition of the Medical Profession in the United States," *Boston Medical and Surgical Journal, 4* (Feb. 15, 1831), 9–10.

Purple, William D., "An Address delivered before the Chenango County Medical Society, Oct. 8, 1839," *Transactions of the Medical Society of the State of New York, 4* (1838–40), 325–34.

"Qualifications for Admission into the Massachusetts Medical Society," *Boston Medical and Surgical Journal, 53* (Oct. 4, 1855), 212–13.

Bibliography

Ramsay, David, *The History of South Carolina from its First Settlement in 1670 to the Year 1808.* Charleston, 1809, 2 vols., 2, ch. 2.

Reichenbach, Charles von, *Physico-Physiological Researches on the Dynamics of Magnetism . . . and Chemism.* Trans. and ed. by John Ashburner. 1st Amer. ed. New York, 1851.

——, *Researches on Magnetism, Electricity, Heat, Light, Crystallization, and Chemical Attraction, in their Relations to Vital Force.* Trans. and ed. by William Gregory. London, 1850.

"Relations between the Clerical and Medical Professions: The Christian Examiner and the Hydropathic Delusion," *Boston Medical and Surgical Journal, 38* (July 26, 1848), 513–20.

Report of a Committee appointed to reply to the Protest of a Minority of the Members of the Medical Society of South Carolina. Charleston, 1835.

Report of the Committee of the Medical Society of the City and County of New York appointed to investigate the subject of a Secret Medical Association. New York, 1831.

Report of Evidence in the Case of John Stephen Bartlett, M. D. versus the Mass. Medical Society. Boston, 1839.

Shattuck, George, "The Medical Profession and Society," *Medical Communications of the Massachusetts Medical Society, 10* (1861–66), 399–430.

Simons, Thomas Y., *A Reply to a Pamphlet by Henry Dickson, M.D.* Charleston, 1834.

Skinner, J. F., "Domestic Medicines," *Boston Medical and Surgical Journal, 40* (May 23, 1849), 309–13.

[Smith, Alban G.], *An Inquiry into the Causes that have Retarded the Prosperity of the Medical College of Ohio.* Cincinnati, 1835.

Smith, Elias, *The Life, Conversion, Preaching, Travels and Sufferings of Elias Smith.* Boston, 1840.

Story, Joseph [?], *An Answer to a Letter addressed to a Republican Member of the House of Representatives of the State of Massachusetts.* Boston, 1812.

Tasistro, L. G., "Modern Female Education," *Godey's Lady's Book, 24* (March 1842), 190–91.

Thomson, Samuel, *Learned Quackery Exposed, or Theory according to art, as Exemplified in the Practice of the Fashionable Doctors of the Present Day.* Boston, 1836.

——, *A Narrative of the Life and Medical Discoveries of Samuel Thomson; Containing an Account of his System of Practice, . . . to which is added An Introduction to his New Guide to Health or Botanic Family Physician; containing the principles upon which the system is founded, with remarks on Fevers, Steaming, Poison, etc.* 4th ed. Columbus, 1827.

——, *New Guide to Health; or Botanic Family Physician. Containing a Complete System of Practice, upon a Plan Entirely New; with a Description of the Vegetables made use of, and Directions for Preparing and Administering Them to Cure Disease, to which is prefixed A Narrative of the Life and Medi-*

cal Discoveries of the Author. 2d ed. Boston, 1825, and Boston edition of 1835 (no ed. number given).

Trial of William Bushnell et al. . . . For Practicing Homoeopathy. . . . Boston, 1873.

Walker, William J., "On the Treatment of Compound and Complicated Fractures," *Medical Communications of the Massachusetts Medical Society,* 7 (1842–48), 171–215.

Waring, Joseph I., ed., *Excerpts of the Minute Book of the Medical Society of South Carolina.* 2 vols. Charleston, 1948.

Warren, John [?], *A Letter Addressed to a Republican Member of the House of Representatives of the State of Massachusetts.* Boston, 1812.

"Why Women were made lovely," *Godey's Lady's Book, 16* (Feb. 1838), 92–93.

PUBLIC DOCUMENTS

MASSACHUSETTS

Acts and Resolves passed by the General Court of Massachusetts, 1802–48. 13 vols. Boston, 1806–48.

A Digest of the Acts of the Commonwealth Relating to the Massachusetts Medical Society, together with the By-Laws and Rules and Orders of the Society and Councillors. Boston, 1861, 1874.

General Laws of Massachusetts from the Adoption of the Constitution to February, 1822. 3 vols. Vols. *1, 2,* Boston, 1823.

Laws of the Commonwealth of Massachusetts, 1812–60, sessional, Boston, 1812–60.

Private and Special Statutes of the Commonwealth of Massachusetts, 1780–1848. 8 vols. Boston, 1805–48.

Revised Statutes of the Commonwealth of Massachusetts, Passed November 4, 1835, Printed under the Supervision of Theron Metcalf and Horace Mann. Boston, 1836.

NEW YORK

Documents of the Assembly of the State of New York, 1830–44, sessional, Albany, 1830–44.

Documents of the Senate of the State of New York, 1830–44, sessional, Albany, 1830–44.

Journal of the Assembly of the State of New York, 1830–44, sessional, Albany, 1830–44.

Journal of the Senate of the State of New York, 1830–44, sessional, Albany, 1830–44.

Laws of the State of New York, 1806–60, sessional, Albany, 1806–60.

Laws of the State of New York Revised and Passed at the 36th session of the Legislature. 2 vols. Albany, 1813.

The Revised Statutes of the State of New York, Passed during the Years One Thousand Eight Hundred and Twenty Seven, and One Thousand Eight Hundred and Twenty Eight; to which are added certain former acts which have not been revised. 3 vols. Albany, 1829.

Bibliography

MARYLAND

Journal of Proceedings of the House of Delegates of Maryland, 1838. Annapolis, 1838.

Journal of Proceedings of the Senate of Maryland, 1838. Annapolis, 1838.

Laws of Maryland Made and Passed at a Session of Assembly Begun and Held at the City of Annapolis on Monday the Third of November in the Year of Our Lord One Thousand Eight Hundred and Eight. Annapolis, 1808.

Laws Made and Passed by the General Assembly of the State of Maryland at an extra session begun and held at the City of Annapolis, on Monday the Fifteenth, and ending on Thursday the eighteenth of June, in the year of Our Lord Eighteen hundred and twelve. Annapolis, 1812.

Laws Made and Passed by the General Assembly of the State of Maryland at the session begun and held at the City of Annapolis on Monday the twenty-sixth of December, 1825. Annapolis, 1825.

Regents of the University of Maryland v. Joseph B. Williams, 9 Gill and Johnson, 365.

SOUTH CAROLINA

Acts and Resolutions of the General Assembly of the State of South Carolina, 1831–60, sessional, Columbia, 1831–60.

Journal of the House of Representatives of the State of South Carolina, 1831–45, sessional, Columbia, 1831–45.

Journal of the Senate of the State of South Carolina, 1831–45, sessional, Columbia, 1831–45.

Statutes at Large of South Carolina. 10 vols. Columbia, 1836–41.

OHIO

Acts of the General Assembly of the State of Ohio, sessional, 1810–39.

Journal of the House of Representatives of the State of Ohio, sessional, 1830–39.

Journal of the Senate of the State of Ohio, sessional, 1830–39.

NEWSPAPERS

Albany Argus, 1843–44.

Baltimore American and Commercial Advertiser, 1826, 1838.

Charleston Mercury, 1831–45.

Charleston Daily Courier, 1826–45.

Cincinnati Advertiser and Ohio Pheonix, 1830–36, 1839–40. Called *Daily Advertiser and Journal* after 1839.

Cincinnati Daily Gazette, 1832–39.

Cincinnati Daily Whig, 1834, 1835–39. Called *Cincinnati Democratic Intelligencer and Commercial Advertiser* from March 1834 to April 1835.

Columbia Free Press, Feb. 5, 1831-Jan. 28, 1832.

Daily Cincinnati Republican, 1837–38.

201

Bibliography

Man (New York), 1834–35.
New England Palladium (Boston), 1805–12.
New York Tribune, 1840–44.
New York Whig, 1831–33, 1839.
Liberty Hall and Cincinnati Gazette, 1818–22.
Western Spy and Literary Cadet, 1820–22.

SECONDARY WORKS

Aaron, Daniel, "Cincinnati, 1818–1838: A Study of Attitudes in the Urban West." Ph.D. dissertation, Harvard, 1942.

Ackerknecht, Erwin H. "Elisha Bartlett and the Philosophy of the Paris Clinical School," *Bulletin of the History of Medicine, 24* (Jan.–Feb. 1950), 42–60.

Akert, Konrad, and Michael P. Hammond, "Emanuel Swedenborg (1688–1772) and His Contributions to Neurology," *Medical History, 6* (July 1962), 255–66.

Beall, Otho T., Jr., and Richard H. Shryock, *Cotton Mather: First Significant Figure in American Medicine*. Baltimore., 1954.

Bell, Whitfield, Jr., *John Morgan: Continental Doctor*. Philadelphia, 1965.

———, "Medical Practice in Colonial America," *Bulletin of the History of Medicine, 31* (Sept.–Oct. 1957), 442–53.

Benson, Lee, *The Concept of Jacksonian Democracy: New York as a Test Case*. Princeton, 1961.

Benton, J. H., et al., *Medical Freedom*. Boston, 1889.

Berman, Alex, "The Impact of the Nineteenth Century Botanico-Medical Movement on American Pharmacy and Medicine." Ph.D. thesis, Pharmacology, University of Wisconsin, 1954.

———, "Neo-Thomsonianism in the United States," *Journal of the History of Medicine and Allied Sciences, 9* (April 1956), 133–55.

———, "A Striving for Scientific Respectability: Some American Botanics and the Nineteenth Century Plant Materia Medica," *Bulletin of the History of Medicine, 30* (Jan.–Feb. 1956), 7–31.

Blake, John B., *Benjamin Waterhouse and the Introduction of Vaccination: A Reappraisal*. Philadelphia, 1957.

Blanton, Wyndham B., *Medicine in Virginia in the Seventeenth Century*. Richmond, 1930.

———, *Medicine in Virginia in the Eighteenth Century*. Richmond, 1931.

Boorstin, Daniel J., *The Americans: The Colonial Experience*. New York, 1958.

Bradford, Thomas L., *Homoeopathic Bibliography of the United States. From the Year 1825 to the Year 1891, Inclusive*. Philadelphia, 1892.

Britten, Emma H., *Modern American Spiritualism: A Twenty Year Record of the Communion Between Earth and the World of Spirits*. New York, 1870.

Burrage, Walter L., *A History of the Massachusetts Medical Society with Biographies of the Founders and Chief Officers, 1781–1922*. P.p., 1923.

Calvin, D. D., *Queen's University at Kingston, 1841–1941*. Kingston, 1941.

Canniff, William, *The Medical Profession in Upper Canada, 1783–1850. An*

Bibliography

Historical Narrative, with Original Documents relating to the Profession, including Some Brief Biographies. Toronto, 1894.

Chapman, John, *The Medical Institutions of the United Kingdom: A History Exemplifying the Evils of Over-Legislation.* London, 1870.

Creighton, Donald, *Dominion of the North: A History of Canada.* Boston, 1944.

Cope, Zachary, *The Royal College of Surgeons of England: A History.* London, 1959.

Copeman, W. S. C., *Doctors and Disease in Tudor Times.* London, 1960.

Cordell, Eugene F., *Historical Sketch of the University of Maryland School of Medicine (1807–1890) with an Introductory Chapter, Notices of the Schools of Law, Arts and Sciences, and Theology, and the Department of Dentistry, and a General Catalogue of Medical Alumni.* Baltimore, 1891.

———, *The Medical Annals of Maryland, 1799–1899.* Baltimore, 1903.

Coventry, Charles B., "History of Medical Legislation in the State of New York," *New York Journal of Medicine, 4* (March 1845), 151–61.

Cross, Whitney, *The Burned-over District: The Social and Intellectual History of Enthusiastic Religion in Western New York, 1800–1850.* Ithaca, 1950.

Davies, John D., *Phrenology, Fad and Science: A Nineteenth Century Crusade.* New Haven, 1955.

"Dr. Ephraim Eliot's Account of the Physicians of Boston," *Proceedings of the Massachusetts Historical Society, 7* (1863–64,), 177–84.

Duffy, John, *The Rudolph Matas History of Medicine in Louisiana.* 2 vols. Baton Rouge, 1958, 1962.

Duncan, Alexander, *Memorials of the Faculty of Physicians and Surgeons of Glasgow, 1599–1850.* Glasgow, 1896.

Duveen, Denis I., and Herbert S. Klickstein, "The Introduction of Lavoisier's Chemical Nomenclature into America," *Isis, 45* (Sept. 1954), pt. 1, 278–92.

Exposition of the Transactions relative to the College of Physicians and Surgeons. New York, 1812.

Felton, H. W., *History of the Eclectic Medical Institute, Cincinnati, Ohio: 1845–1902.* Cincinnati, 1902.

Fitz, Reginald H., "The Legislative Control of Medical Practice," *Boston Medical and Surgical Journal, 130* (June 28, 1894), 637–41.

———, *Rise and Fall of the Licensed Physician in Massachusetts, 1781–1860.* Reprinted from the *Transactions of the Association of American Physicians,* 1894.

Fleming, Donald, *John William Draper and the Religion of Science.* Philadelphia, 1950.

———, *William H. Welch and the Rise of Modern Medicine.* Boston, 1954.

Flexner, Abraham, *Medical Education in the United States and Canada: A Report to the Carnegie Foundation for the Advancement of Learning.* New York, 1910.

Gibbons, Peter D., "The Berkshire Medical Institution," *Bulletin of the History of Medicine, 38* (Jan.-Feb. 1964), 45–64.

Goodall, Charles, *The Royal College of Physicians of London founded and established by Law; as appears by Letters, Patents, Acts of Parliament; adjudged Cases, etc., and An Historical Account of the College's proceedings against Empirics and unlicensed Practitioners in every Princes Reign from their first Incorporation to the Murther of the Royal Martyr, King Charles the First.* London, 1684.

Goodfield, G. J., *The Growth of Scientific Physiology: Physiological Method and the Mechanist-Vitalist Controversy, Illustrated by the Problems of Respiration and Animal Heat.* London, 1960.

Gray, John F., *Early Annals of Homoeopathy in New York.* New York, 1863.

Hall, Courtney R., *A Scientist of the Early Republic: Samuel Latham Mitchell, 1764–1831.* New York, 1934.

Handlin, Oscar and Mary F., *Commonwealth: A Study of the Role of Government in the American Economy: Massachusetts, 1774–1861.* New York, 1947.

———, "Origins of the American Business Corporation," *Journal of Economic History,* 5 (May 1945), 1–23.

Harrington, Thomas F., *The Harvard Medical School: A History, Narrative and Documentary, 1782–1905,* ed. James Mumford, 3 vols. New York, 1905.

Heagerty, John Joseph, *Four Centuries of Medical History in Canada.* Toronto, 1928.

Heaton, Claude R., "Medicine in New York during the English Colonial Period, 1664–1775," *Bulletin of History of Medicine, 17* (Jan. 1945), 9–37.

Historical Bulletin: Calgary Associate Clinic, 1943–56. Vols. 9–22.

A History of New York Kappa Lambda Conspiracy. New York, 1839.

Holmes, Oliver Wendell, "Homoeopathy and its Kindred Delusions" and "The Medical Profession in Massachusetts," *Medical Essays, 1842–1882, 9 in* Writings of Oliver Wendell Holmes. Boston, 1891, 1–102, 312–69.

Horine, Emmet F., *Daniel Drake (1785–1852): Pioneer Physician of the Midwest.* Philadelphia, 1961.

Hosack, Alexander E., *A Memoir of the Late David Hosack, M.D.* Philadelphia, 1861.

Jordan, Philip D., "The Secret Six, An Inquiry into the Basic Materia Medica of the Thomsonian System of Botanic Medicine," *Ohio State Archaeological and Historical Quarterly, 52* (Oct.-Dec. 1943), 347–55.

Joy, Robert J. T., "The Natural Bonesetters with Special Reference to the Sweet Family," *Bulletin of the History of Medicine, 28* (Sept.-Oct. 1954), 416–41.

Juettner, Otto, *Daniel Drake and His Followers. Historical and Biographical Sketches.* Cincinnati, 1909.

Kett, Joseph F., "Provincal Medical Practice in England, 1730–1815," *Journal of the History of Medicine and Allied Sciences, 19* (January 1964), 17–29.

King, William H., ed., *History of Homoeopathy and its Institutions in America.* 4 vols. New York, 1905.

Kneer, Calvin, *Life of Hering.* Philadelphia, 1940.

Konold, Donald E., *A History of American Medical Ethics, 1847–1912.* Madison, 1962.

Bibliography

Lane, William C., *Dr. Benjamin Waterhouse and Harvard University*. Reprinted from *Proceedings of the Cambridge Historical Society, 4* (Jan. 1909).

Langstaff, John Brett, *Doctor Bard of Hyde Park: The Famous Physician of Revolutionary Times, The Man Who Saved Washington's Life*. New York, 1942.

Lawrie, James Adair. *Letters on the Charters of the Scotch Universities and Medical Corporations and Medical Reform in Scotland*. Glasgow, 1856.

Leake, Chauncy D., "A Gentleman Physician of New York: Dr. David Hosack: The Great American Practitioner of the Early Nineteenth Century." MS, New York Academy of Medicine.

———, "What was Kappa Lambda?" *Annals of Medical History, 4* (Summer 1922), 192–206.

Long, Esmond R., *A History of Pathology*. Baltimore, 1928.

Malone, Dumas, *The Public Life of Thomas Cooper*. New Haven, 1926.

Mitchell, Samuel L., *A Discourse on the Life and Character of Samuel Bard*. New York, 1821.

Moore, Thomas E., Jr., "The Early Years of the Harvard Medical School," *Bulletin of the History of Medicine, 28* (Nov.–Dec. 1953), 540–42.

Naylor, Mildred V., "Sylvester Graham, 1794–1851," *Annals of Medical History*, 3 ser., *4* (May 1942), 236–40.

Newman, Charles, *The Evolution of Medical Education in the Nineteenth Century*. London, 1957.

Norwood, William F., *Medical Education in the United States before the Civil War*. Philadelphia, 1944.

Noyes, John Humphrey, *History of American Socialisms*. Philadelphia, 1870.

Packard, Francis R., *History of Medicine in the United States*. New York, 1931.

Patterson, Robert G., "The Role of the 'District' as a Unit in Organized Medicine in Ohio," *Ohio State Archaeological and Historical Quarterly, 49* (1940), 366–77.

Pickard, Madge E., and R. Carlyle Buley, *The Midwest Pioneer: His Ills, Cures, and Doctors*. Crawfordsville, Indiana, 1945.

Podmore, Frank, *Mesmerism and Christian Science: A Short History of Mental Healing*. 1st Amer. ed. Philadelphia, 1909.

———, *Modern Spiritualism*. 2 vols. London, 1902.

Potter, Nathaniel, *Some Account of the Rise and Progress of the University of Maryland*. Baltimore, 1838.

Poynter, F. N. L., ed., *The Evolution of Medical Practice in Britain*. London, 1961.

Raach, John H., *A Directory of English Country Physicians, 1603–1643*. London, 1962.

Rivington, Walter, *The Medical Profession*. Dublin, 1879.

Robbins, Christine C., *David Hosack, Citizen of New York. Memoirs of the American Philosophical Society, 62*. Philadelphia, 1964.

Roberts, R. S., "The Apothecary in the Seventeenth Century," *Pharmaceutical Journal, 108* (Nov. 24, 1962), 505–09.

Bibliography

Roberts, R. S., "The Personnel and Practice of Medicine in Tudor and Stuart England. Part I. The Provinces," *Medical History, 6* (Oct. 1962), 363–81.

———, "The Personnel and Practice of Medicine in Tudor and Stuart England. Part II. London," *Medical History, 7* (July 1964), 217–34.

Rogers, Fred. B., "Nicholas Romayne, 1756–1817: Stormy Petrel of the American Medical Profession," *Journal of Medical Education, 35* (March 1960), 258–63.

Rosen, George, *Fees and Fee Bills: Some Economic Aspects of Medical Practice in Nineteenth Century America.* Reprinted from *Supplements to the Bulletin of the History of Medicine,* no. 6, 1946.

Shafer, Henry B., *The American Medical Profession, 1783 to 1850.* New York, 1936.

Shira, Donald D., "The Legal Requirements for Medical Practice—An Attempt to Regulate by Law and the Purpose Behind the Movement," *Ohio State Archaeological and Historical Quarterly, 48* (1939), 181–88.

———, "The Organization of the Ohio State Medical Society and its relation to the Ohio Medical Convention," *Ohio State Archaeological and Historical Quarterly, 50* (1941), 366–71.

Shryock, Richard H., *Medicine and Society in America, 1660–1860.* New York, 1960.

———, "Public Relations of the Medical Profession in Great Britain and the United States: 1600–1870," *Annals of Medical History, 2* (May 1930), 308–39.

Stookey, Byron, *A History of Colonial Medical Education in the Province of New York with its Subsequent Development (1767–1830).* Springfield, Ill., 1962.

Tyler, Alice Felt, *Freedom's Fermant: Phases of American Social History.* Minneapolis, 1944.

Van Ingen, Philip, *The New York Academy of Medicine: Its First Hundred Years.* New York, 1949.

———, "Remarks on 'Kappa Lambda, Elf or Ogre' and a little more concerning the Society," *Bulletin of the History of Medicine, 18* (Dec. 1945), 513–38.

Viets, Henry, *A Brief History of Medicine in Massachusetts.* Boston, 1930.

Waite, Frederick C., "American Sectarian Medical Colleges before the Civil War," *Bulletin of the History of Medicine, 19* (Feb. 1946), 148–66.

———, "The First Medical Diploma Mill in the United States," *Bulletin of the History of Medicine, 20* (Nov. 1946), 495–504.

———, "The First Sectarian Medical School in New England," *New England Journal of Medicine, 207* (Dec. 1, 1932), 984–88.

———, *History of the New England Female Medical College, 1848–1874.* Boston, 1950.

———, "The Professional Education of Pioneer Ohio Physicians," *Ohio State Archaeological and Historical Quarterly, 48* (1939), 189–97.

———, "Thomsonianism in Ohio," *Ohio State Archaeological and Historical Quarterly, 49* (Oct.-Dec. 1940), 322–31.

Walsh, James J., *History of Medicine in New York.* 5 vols. New York, 1919.

Bibliography

Waring, Joseph I., et al., *A Brief History of the South Carolina Medical Association. To Which Are Added Short Historical Sketches of Various Medical Institutions and Societies of South Carolina.* Charleston, 1948.

———, *A History of Medicine in South Carolina, 1670–1825.* Charleston, 1964.

Wilder, Alexander, *History of Medicine: A Brief Outline of Medical History and Sects of Physicians, From the Earliest Historical Period with an Extended Account of the Healing Art in the Nineteenth Century and Especially of the American Eclectic Practice of Medicine, Never before published.* New Sharon, Me., 1901.

Willcock, J. W., *The Laws relating to the Medical Profession.* London, 1830.

Young, James Harvey, *The Toadstool Millionaires: A Social History of Patent Medicines in America before Federal Regulation.* Princeton, 1961.

INDEX

Index

Index

Howe, Julia W., 154
Huger, Daniel, 116
Hunt, Harriet K., 120
Hunter, John, 142, 144
Hunterian Museum, 142
Hutchinson, Anne, 6
Hydropathy, 161

Indian doctors, 123
Indiana, University of, 176 n
Institutions: weakness of in America, 30; medical, 30–31. *See also* Licensing legislation; Medical education; Medical profession; Medical societies

Jackson, Andrew, ix, 110–11
Jackson, James, 77–78
Jahn, Friedrich L., 136
Jahr, Gottlieb, 137
James VI, 33
James, Henry, 155
Jameson, Horatio G. 51
Jefferson, Thomas, 111
Jefferson Medical College, 67, 111
Jeffries, John, 75
Jenner, Edward, 74
Jervey, J. P., 112
Johns Hopkins University, 58
Johnson, Reverdy, 53 n, 54
Johnstone, F. U., 113

Kappa Lambda: founding, 112; hostility toward, 112–14
Kast, Thomas, 14
King, Mitchel, 61
King, Thomas S., 154
King's College. *See* Columbia University; College of Physicians and Surgeons
Knoop, Nicholas, 97

Laplace, Pierre Simon de, 149
Larkin, Lyman, 25, 26
Lawrence, William, 142–43
Lee, Arthur, 11
Lee, Richard H., 11

Lettsom, John, 72, 74
Lewis, Thatcher, 93
Licensing legislation: in England, 4–5; in colonial America, 7–8, 12; in frontier states, 13; repeal, 13; in older states, 12–13; in Massachusetts, 14–16, 24–30; in New York, 16–17, 20–22, 40–43; in South Carolina, 16–19, 22–23, 64; in Maryland, 19, 22; in Ohio, 19–20, 23–24, 93–94; in Scotland, 33–35; in Canada West, 65; relation to medical education, 69; assumption behind, 97; as pointless, 163
Linacre, Thomas, 2, 30
Lloyd, James, 14
Lobelia, 101, 107
London, University of, 34
Lord, Thomas, 7
Louis, Pierre, 156, 158, 160
Louisville Medical Institute, 90
Lucas, Governor, 92
Lytle, Robert T., 91

McClellan, George, 114
McDowell, Ephraim, 86
McDowell, Joseph N., 86
McGill University, 66 n, 67
Mackenzie, William L., 66
McKim, Isaac, 51 ff
Macneven, William, 40
Manley, John R., 113
Marriott, William H., 52
Marshall, John, 54–55
Maryland: licensing legislation, 19, 22, 169; medical education in, 46–59, 95. *See also* Medical and Chirurgical Faculty of Maryland
Maryland, University of, 47, 95; proprietary nature of, 46–50; trustees, 50–56, 59; confiscation, 50; liberal arts faculty, 51 n; legality of confiscation, 54–56; regents, 55–56, 59
Massachusetts, 13; licensing, 24–30; medical education in, 71–77; district societies, 77–79; Thomsonianism in, 106; homoeopathy in, 138; *vis medicatrix naturae* in, 159. *See also* Harvard Medical Institution; Massachusetts Medical Society

212

Index

Massachusetts College of Physicians, 75–77

Massachusetts General Hospital, 24

Massachusetts Medical Society: incorporation, 12, 14; early history, 14–16; police power, 25–26; homoeopathy in, 26–29; end of licensing monopoly, 28; and medical education, 72–77; district societies of, 78–79. *See also* Harvard Medical Institution; Berkshire Medical Institution; Waterhouse, Benjamin

Mather, Cotton, 6

Medical and Chirurgical Faculty of Maryland, 46, 50, 57, 58; early history, 19; and College of Medicine of Maryland, 46–47; later history, 168. *See also* Maryland, University of

Medical College of Ohio, 95; incorporation, 81; proprietary nature, 81–82; early feuds within, 82–84; expulsion of Drake, 84–85; return of Drake, 86–87; Drake's resignation, 87–89; trustees, 88–89; and Cincinnati College, 90–91; low quality, 93; control of district society, 94. *See also* Drake, Daniel

Medical College of South Carolina: creation, 59–60; and Medical Society of South Carolina, 61–63; rivalry with Medical College of State of South Carolina, 64–65; causes of failure, 95–96. *See also* Medical Society of South Carolina

Medical College of the State of South Carolina, 172; creation, 62; success, 63–64, 95–96

Medical degrees: as licenses to practice, 32–33, 45–46

Medical education: in England, 32–33; New York, 35–46; Maryland, 46–59; South Carolina, 59–64; Canada, 66–69; Massachusetts, 71–79; Ohio, 79–94; Thomsonian attitude, 107, 130; and women, 120; attitude of homoeopathy, 137, 164; distinctive aspects in America, 171–72. *See also* Harvard Medical Institution; Medical College of Ohio; Medical College of South Carolina; Medical College of State of South Carolina; College of Physicians and Surgeons; Maryland, University of

Medical ethics, 25–26

Medical legislation. *See* Licensing legislation

Medical profession: in Tudor–Stuart England, 1–5; in colonial America, 5–10; and decay of European institutions, 30–31; in 19th-century Scotland, 32–35; American and Canadian professions compared, 65–68; evaluation, 68–69; conservatism of, 112–14; fees, 114–15; and women, 118, 120; reaction to repeal of licensing, 165–68; significance of Thomsonianism for, 131; significance of homoeopathy for, 163–64; and voluntary associations, 168–69, 172–77; stability of, 178–80. *See also* Licensing legislation; Medical education; Medical societies

Medical science: as art and cunning, 4; and empiricism, 9; significance of homoeopathy for, 156–64. *See also* Orthodox medicine

Medical societies: establishment, 13; rivalry with medical schools in Scotland, 32–35; Daniel Drake on, 45–46; and medical schools in New York, 35–45; in South Carolina, 59–61; and Canada, 64; in Massachusetts, 72–77; in Ohio, 93–94; voluntary, 168–77; functions, 180. *See also* Medical education

Medical Society of South Carolina: establishment, 17; early history, 18; and Medical College of South Carolina, 59–60; trustees, 60–61; effects of professional rivalries on, 64. *See also* Medical College of South Carolina

Medical Society of the County of New York, 36, 168; and establishment of College of Physicians and Surgeons, 36; declining influence over college, 38–40; and *Circular Letter*, 41; and new medical school, 44–45. *See also* College of Physicians and Surgeons

213

Index

Memminger, C. G., 116

Meredith, Jonathan, 50

Mesmer, Anton, 142, 149

Mesmerism, 161, 179; and homoeopathy, 141–42; and electricity, 144–46; on matter and spirit, 149; and Swedenborgianism, 150. *See also* Homoeopathy; Swedenborgianism

Miami University medical faculty, 86

Millerism, 129

Mitchell, Thomas D., 86–87

Mitchill, Samuel L., 35 ff, 43

Montreal Medical Institute, 66 n

Moorhead, John, 80, 82–85, 87

Morgan, John, 10, 11; professional ideals, 10; *Discourse,* 10; and national College of Physicians, 11

Morton, W. T. G., 174

Mott, Valentine, 40, 168, 174

Motta, Jacob de la, 60

Nardin, D. F., 23, 124

Natural bonesetters, 123

Nature: and Thomsonianism, 122–24; and other sects, 123–24; and clergy, 124

Nature philosophy, 144

Neo-Thomsonianism, 120, 130

Neurology. *See* Buchanan, Joseph R.

New England Botanico-Medical College, 78

New England Female Medical College, 122

New Hampshire: homoeopathy in, 140

New Orleans: homoeopathy in, 140

New York: licensing in, 12, 13, 16–17, 20–22, 165; medical education in, 35–45; Thomsonianism in, 106, 129; homoeopathy in, 135, 140–41; voluntary associations in, 168–69, 173–74. *See also* Medical Society of the County of New York; Columbia University; College of Physicians and Surgeons

New York Academy of Medicine, 168–69, 174

New York Dispensary, 113

New York Hospital, 113

New York University Medical College, 44

North American College of the Homoeopathic Healing Art. *See* Allentown Academy

Nostrums, 100

Ohio: licensing in, 13, 19–20, 23–24; medical education in, 79–94; institutional control in, 94–96; Thomsonianism in, 106; homoeopathy in, 138; voluntary associations in, 169, 174–76. *See also* Medical College of Ohio

Ohio Medical Convention, 81, 169

Ohio State Medical Society, 169, 174–75

Oken, Lorenz, 144, 154

O'Neall, John B., 61

Orthodox medicine: and John Brown, 101–02; compared to Thomsonianism, 101–02; concept of, 161–63

Oxford University, 32

Packard, Francis R., 8 n

Paracelsus, 110

Paris School, 156–57

Parker, Theodore, 154

Parker, Willard, 89

Patent medicines, 174

Pattison, Granville S., 49, 52, 58

Peabody, A. P., 124

Peabody, Elizabeth P., 154

Pecker, James, 14

Penn Medical College, 121

Penn, Thomas, 11

Pennsylvania: homoeopathy in, 136–37

Pennsylvania, University of: medical department, 10, 38, 172

Percival, Thomas, 26

Perfectionism: and clergy, 127; **and** homoeopathy, 154–55

Perkinism, 97–100

Perkins, Benjamin D., 97 ff

Perkins, Elisha, 97–98, 102

Perry, Benjamin, 112, 116

Phillips, Wendell, 154

Phrenology, 161, 179; and homoeopathy, 142; origin, 146; on matter and spirit, 149

214

Index

Sturm, William, 138
Surgeon-apothecary, 5, 118
Surgeons, 2
Swaim, William, 100
Swedenborg, Emanuel, 149–50, 153
Swedenborgianism: appeal to Americans, 149–50; and mesmerism, 150; and homoeopathy, 150–53; and Transcendentalism, 153–54
Sweet family, 123

Taney, Roger B., 50, 52, 54
Tappen, Peter, 39
Tasistro, L. G., 118 f
Thacher, Thomas, 6
Thomson, Cyrus, 106
Thomson, John, 20, 106, 119
Thomson, Samuel, 20, 21, 56, 57, 78, 122, 125; early career, 100–03; system, 101; prosecution, 102; secures a patent, 102–03; compared with Elias Smith, 104–05; personality, 104–05; and Andrew Jackson, 110–11; nationalism, 122; contradiction, 129–30; death, 130
Thomsonianism, 20, 21, 56, 57: spread, 106–07; as political theory, 107–11; 115–16; and women, 117, 119, 120; defense of nature, 122–24, 125; nationalism, 122; perfectionism, 124–28; and clergy, 124–28; and millennialism, 128–29; transformation and decline, 130; and domestic practice, 130; compared with homoeopathy, 139–41; replaced by homoeopathy, 163–64; significance of decline, 178–79
Tocqueville, Alexis de, ix
Toronto School of Medicine, 66, 67
Toronto, University of, 67
Township Trustees, 87, 90, 92, 93
Transcendental Club, 109
Transcendentalism, 153–54
Transylvania University, 85
Trinity University, 67 n
Turnbull, Robert J., 61
Turner, Frederick J., ix

Union and States Rights Party, 116
Union College, 41, 142 n

United States Army Medical Corps, 31
University of Maryland v. Joseph B. Williams, 54 n
University of the State of New York, 36, 39–40

Vermont: homoeopathy in, 140
Victoria University, 67
"Vindex" letters. *See* Smith, Alban G.
Vis medicatrix naturae, 125, 158–59
Vitalism, 161; and homoeopathy, 133–34; in England, 142–44
Voluntary associations: need for, 168–69; failure of, 172–77

Wagner, John, 60
Ware, John, 172
Warren, Abigail C., 71
Warren, John, 10, 14; and establishment of Harvard Medical Institution, 71–72; dislike for Waterhouse, 74; opposition to Massachusetts College of Physicians, 76–77
Warren, John C., 24, 146; conflict with Waterhouse, 73, 75–76
Warren, Joseph, 71
Washington, George, 71
Washington Medical College, 51
Waterhouse, Benjamin, 72; feuds with fellow professors, 72, 73; on removal to Boston, 73–74; dislike for John Warren, 74–75; and Massachusetts College of Physicians, 75–77
Watts, John, 12, 42, 43
Webster, Daniel, 54, 109
Welch, William H., vii, 69
Wesselhoeft, William, 136, 154–55
Whig Party: and licensing in Maryland, 56–57; and licensing in New York, 115
Whitman, Josiah, 85
Whitman, Walt, 146
Williams, John, 25
Williams, Nathaniel, 50, 52
Williams, Thomas, 75
Willoughby Medical College, 175
Wilson, Abraham D., 135
Winchester, George, 50

216